LIGHT FOR THE WORLD
Edison and the Power Industry

This book is not just another biograph···
Rather it is a simultaneous biography···
inventor and his greatest invention—th···
power distribution that gave electric light···

Starting with Sir William Gilbert, Cou···
to Queen Elizabeth I, Mr. Silverberg tells a fascinating story of our growing knowledge of electricity and
what it does, through Volta, Ampère, Faraday, and
Franklin, down to Edison and his contemporary
competitors, Tesla and Westinghouse.

Everyone is familiar with Edison, the inventor and
his major contribution: the incandescent light bulb,
the phonograph, the motion picture. Few people realize that he was also an astute promotor who, in
order to gain acceptance for his lamp, had to invent
dynamos, cables, insulators, conductors, voltage regulators, junction boxes, meters, fuses, and fittings
—everything, in fact, necessary to turn his invention
from an incredible curiosity into a practical—inex-
pensive and safe—tool. Electric light for the world
was his first objective; creation of an industry followed. Edison's inventions opened the way to sub-
ways, traffic lights, elevators, air conditioners, radio,
television, and night baseball games. As some
30,000,000 inhabitants of northeastern United States
discovered in November, 1965, when the power stops,
the world stops.

Mr. Silverberg has salted the book liberally with
extracts from contemporary accounts of the great,
rough-hewn man; and from Edison's notebooks—
revealing his pungent wit, his amazing grasp of the
problems surrounding practical application of his inventions, including financing. Jay Gould, J. Pierpont
Morgan, Vanderbilt, Twombly, Insull, and Villard
were all his familiars. Morgan, in fact, went to see
Edison in his Menlo Park laboratory when Edison
was too busy to go see Morgan. There is also an ap-
pealing vignette—gas lit, the quiet broken only by the
clopping of horses' hooves—of a world before electricity in all its subdivision became a fact of modern life.

2189

···OUT THE AUTHOR

···VERBERG is the author of more
···ctual books, many of which are
···gical, historical, or scientific
···ugh most of these books were
···ally for young people, they have
···ularity among adult readers.

···nt successes include *Lost Cities*
··· *Civilizations*, an Honor Book in
··· York *Herald-Tribune* Children's
···; *The Auk, the Dodo, and the*
···or Book in *Book Week's* 1967
···ok Festival; and *The Old Ones:*
··· *American Southwest*, which was
···the ten best books of the year for
···in 1965 by the National Associ-
···endent Schools.

LIGHT FOR

D. VAN NOSTRAND *Company, Inc.*

ROBERT SILVERBERG

THE WORLD
Edison
and the
Power Industry

Princeton, New Jersey   Toronto   London   Melbourne

for Joe Elder

VAN NOSTRAND REGIONAL OFFICES: *New York, Chicago, San Francisco*

D. VAN NOSTRAND COMPANY, LTD., *London*

D. VAN NOSTRAND COMPANY, (Canada), LTD., *Toronto*

D. VAN NOSTRAND AUSTRALIA PTY., LTD., *Melbourne*

Illustrations appearing between pages 134 and 135 are used
with the permission of the United States Department of the
Interior, National Park Service, Edison National Historic Site,
Orange, New Jersey.

Contents

v

"WE will make electric light so cheap that only the rich will be able to burn candles."

—Edison

Light's Golden Jubilee

THE summer of 1929 was a time of electric excitement in the
United States, in more ways than one. The nation, under newly-
elected President Hoover, was enjoying dizzy prosperity. A
financier named John J. Raskob had written a much-discussed
magazine article, "Everybody Ought to be Rich," explaining
how investing in sound common stocks could make anyone a
millionaire. The stock market, after a brief swoon in March, was
climbing astonishingly: a rise of 110 points in the New York
Times index of industrial stocks, from 339 to 449, between the
last day of May and the last day of August. General Electric was
up from 268 to 391, Westinghouse from 151 to 286, American
Telephone from 209 to 303. Babe Ruth was hitting home runs by
the dozen for the New York Yankees, but Connie Mack's Philadelphia Athletics were moving invincibly toward the American
League championship. The Graf Zeppelin was on its first round-
the-world flight. Transcontinental Air Transport had recently
inaugurated forty-eight-hour coast-to-coast service, via a combination of planes and trains. Erich Maria Remarque's *All Quiet
on the Western Front* and Sinclair Lewis' *Dodsworth* were the
best-selling books.

In West Orange, New Jersey, an ailing old man named Thomas Alva Edison was tinkering with a scheme for extracting commercial-grade rubber from goldenrod and other weeds. And in other parts of the country, rival groups were separately planning a celebration of the fiftieth anniversary of a far more successful Edison invention: the incandescent light bulb.

Early in the morning of October 21, 1879, Edison had sent a current of electricity through a carbon filament within an experimental glass globe. From the bulb came a dim but steady reddish glow. As the inventor and his men watched in sleepless wonder, the bulb burned on and on, through the night and through the dawn, until after many hours of consecutive service it finally winked out. It was the culmination of a year and a half of hard work; yet for Edison that day was really only the beginning of a much larger enterprise. Now that he had a light bulb that could be used in the home, he could go on to develop a system of generating, transmitting, and distributing electricity—a system unlike anything that had gone before. He could offer light to the world, and power as well.

So had he done. That first flickering, fading bulb had been followed by billions more. The wheels of industry now turned electrically; electricity brought voices through the air, cast images on a screen, slew darkness a trillion times a night. Thomas Edison had made electricity into man's most useful servant.

Monuments to Edison's achievement were scattered everywhere. Dozens of power companies included the inventor's name in theirs: New York Edison Company, Brooklyn Edison, Chicago's Commonwealth Edison, Southern California Edison, Toledo Edison, Detroit Edison, Missouri Edison, Boston Edison, and so on across the land. For their customers, the monthly light bill served as a reminder of Edison's achievement. Then there was the vast General Electric Company. Supplier of electrical equipment to much of the nation, G.E. was the direct descendant of Edison's original machine shop. The inventor had long since given up any financial interest in these companies. He had sold out and turned his attention to other miracles: the phonograph and motion pictures, most notably. But it was with the electric light that Edison's name was inextricably bound.

As the golden jubilee of the first successful light bulb approached, General Electric proposed to celebrate it with a great public festival. The idea had come from a loosely organized group of Edison's old laboratory workers and friends, the "Edison Pioneers." The Pioneers had long given annual luncheon meetings in honor of the inventor's birthday, but 1929 seemed to call for some special event. Lacking the funds themselves to stage a properly grandiose jamboree, the Pioneers turned to General Electric.

Edison's relationship with G.E. had been awkward for many years. True, he was the ancestral deity of the company, and still was hailed in G.E. publicity as the founder. But by a corporate reshuffling in 1892 he had quietly been pushed from control of what was then the Edison General Electric Company, and his name had been dropped from the banner. When he visited G.E.'s huge Schenectady plant in 1922, it was the first time he had been in a G.E. factory in twenty-five years. And in recent negotiations between G.E. and Edison's own manufacturing company over the rights to certain radio patents, G.E. had been anything but kind to the founding father.

Past differences seemed to pale as the jubilee year arrived, though. To G.E., it seemed appropriate to honor the old man on October 21. A young public-relations man named Edward Bernays—the nephew of another great figure of the era, Sigmund Freud—was chosen to organize the event.

Bernays sketched plans for a series of public banquets in various cities, reaching a climax with a huge affair at Schenectady on October 21, at which Edison himself would re-enact his 1879 work and light a replica of his first lamp. These plans were well along toward completion before anyone bothered to notify the inventor of the part he was supposed to play.

Edison was eighty-two years old, deaf, and frail. He had always been skeptical of the value of banquets, commemorative medals, festivals, and other such demonstrations. With time engulfing him, and the rubber-from-goldenrod scheme still unrealized, he had little wish to join G.E.'s project—particularly since its main purpose appeared to be to push the sale of General Electric products, and he felt little affection for that corporation. So Edison hesitated, unwilling to spoil the jubilee festival, but reluctant to allow himself to be exploited this way.

He was rescued by his oldest, closest, and wealthiest friend, Henry Ford. An Edison associate notified the auto magnate that G.E. intended to "commercialize" the anniversary celebration. Ford hurried east and presented himself unexpectedly at Edison's West Orange mansion. "I'll show 'em," Ford declared. "I'll kidnap the whole party!" Without much difficulty, he persuaded Edison to let him stage the jubilee.

Ford, sixteen years Edison's junior, idolized the great inventor. Edison was the man who had invented almost everything; Ford, who had concentrated all his energies on a single project, carrying it to perfection, envied and admired his friend's universality. His admiration took the form of creating an open-air museum at Dearborn, Michigan, in which buildings associated with Edison's career had pride of place. The Dearborn museum was intended to be a mirror for American life and ingenuity. Ford had purchased and brought to it such things as a courthouse where Lincoln had practiced law; a typical log cabin; a typical general store; the little schoolhouse where he himself had been educated; and the office of the botanist Luther Burbank. His prize acquisitions, though, were the Edison buildings: the Edison family homestead, the Michigan railway station where Edison had worked in boyhood, and the famous laboratory from Menlo Park, New Jersey, where the incandescent bulb had been invented.

All these treasures were rapidly being installed, and Ford would be ready to dedicate his "Edison Institute" in the fall of 1929. What better time than on the fiftieth anniversary day itself?

The officials of General Electric were horrified to learn that Ford had snatched their festival and its hero away from them. There were frantic conferences, and at last a face-saving compromise: the ceremony would be held at Dearborn, but under the joint sponsorship of Ford and G.E.

Bernays continued to round up dignitaries for the transferred jubilee. Ford personally took charge of the Dearborn end of the planning. Somehow the idea came to him that it would be appropriate to hold the dedication in the building in which the Declaration of Independence had been signed; so he hired an architect and sent him to Philadelphia to see about the purchase of Independence Hall. The architect returned with the news that Independence Hall was not for sale. Unruffled, Ford said, "Then build me a perfect replica of Independence Hall that will last three times as long as the original. Build the foundation three times as deep and three times as wide as the one in Philadelphia. That'll show 'em!"

Amid the farm cottages, log cabins, and transplanted streets of Ford's museum there hurriedly rose the replica of Independence Hall, covering eight acres but identical in appearance to the smaller original building. Several streets away—beyond the Henry Ford birthplace and an old grist mill—Edison's Menlo Park laboratory was reassembled and restored. Edison had abandoned Menlo Park in the 1880's, casually allowing the historic buildings to fall into decay. But Ford had every rotten plank replaced, and carefully put tools and instruments on the shelves again. He had even brought carloads of soil and shrubbery from New Jersey to provide the last touch in authenticity.

On October 19, two days before the big event, Edison arrived at Dearborn. He was pale and shaky from an August attack of pneumonia that had placed his life in danger, but his spirits

5

soared when he saw the reborn Menlo Park. Grinning broadly, he wandered through the old laboratory, the office, the machine shop, the library, seeing again his dynamos, his bulbs, his array of electrical equipment. "Hmm," he exclaimed, "the same damn old New Jersey clay!" The care with which everything had been duplicated amazed him. At length he turned to his friend.

"Ford," he said, "it's ninety-nine and nine-tenths perfect."

Ford wanted to know where the restoration had gone astray.

"Oh, our floor was never as clean as this," Edison told him.

Bernays, too, had done his work well. To Dearborn came such people as Albert Einstein, Orville Wright, Madame Curie, Will Rogers. Representing the world of finance were John D. Rockefeller, Jr., J. P. Morgan the younger, Otto Kahn, Thomas W. Lamont, and others. President Herbert Hoover attended, as did several members of the Cabinet. This, after all, was the jubilee of America's most potent industry, the one that gave power to all the others.

President Hoover arrived by special train on the 21st. The Presidential party was met by Mr. and Mrs. Ford and Mr. and Mrs. Edison. At a transfer point they changed to a wood-burning replica of the Grand Trunk Railway train on which Edison had sold candy and magazines during the Civil War. The little train chugged half a mile down its narrow track to a restoration of the Smith's Creek Junction station. There, seventy years before, Edison had supposedly been heaved from the train by an irate conductor after his little chemical laboratory had started a fire in the baggage car.

The assembled celebrities were waiting there—along with a milling mob of reporters and guards. As Edward Bernays tells it:

> Nobody seemed to be in charge, so I pushed into the crowd and yelled for the "gentlemen please to move back, form a line and meet the President in orderly fashion." I stood opposite Mr. Hoover. As the line moved slowly between us, I asked the name of each approaching man and repeated it

to the President. This was a detail none of us had foreseen and for which no plan had been made. What should have been a dignified ceremony of greeting the President of the United States was turning into a shambles. Near the front of the line was a man whose face was vaguely familiar. As he came along in his turn I asked him, "Your name please?" "John D. Rockefeller Jr.," he answered in a low voice.

I introduced him to the President, struck by the fact that I was introducing John D. Rockefeller Jr. to the President of the United States, although I had not met either of them before.

Confusion gave way to pathos a few minutes later. A trainboy handed Edison a basket of goods; then, as had been arranged, Edison offered his merchandise to the President, crying, "Candy, apples, sandwiches, and newspapers!" Perhaps it was a triumph of publicity, but to those present it seemed a tasteless and embarrassing imposition on the old man.

On through the day went the round of events, while Edison grew steadily wearier. At 6:15 that evening the five hundred distinguished guests gathered in Ford's Independence Hall to hear toastmaster Owen D. Young, the chairman of General Electric's board of directors, deliver a formal welcoming address. Then the entire assemblage moved on to the restored Menlo Park laboratory for the re-enactment of the great moment of 1879.

Edison stepped out onto the second floor of the building and showed how he had charred a piece of thread and inserted it into a vacuum globe. The guests watched tensely as the trembling fingers performed familiar manipulations. Graham Mc-Namee, the ubiquitous radio voice of the day, told millions of fascinated listeners:

"The lamp is now ready, as it was half a century ago! Will it light? Will it burn? Edison touches the wire. . . . Ladies and gentlemen—*it lights!* Light's Golden Jubilee has come to a triumphant climax!"

7

All over the nation, special lamps blazed up simultaneously as McNamee's resonant voice proclaimed:

"And Edison said: *'Let there be light!'* "

It was a properly dramatic moment. Now the guests returned to Independence Hall for the concluding banquet. But Edison had had enough of this play-acting. At the door of the banquet hall he faltered and nearly collapsed. Taken to a sofa in the corridor, he wept with fatigue and muttered to his wife, "I won't go in! I won't go in!"

Some warm milk was brought. It seemed to revive him, and he entered the hall, taking his place of honor on the dais. Too deaf to hear what was being said, he waited grimly through an endless series of congratulatory speeches. Eventually it was President Hoover's turn:

> I have thought it fitting for the President of the United States to take part in paying honor to one of our great Americans. . . . Mr. Edison . . . has repelled the darkness . . . has brought to our country great distinction throughout the world. He has brought benefaction to all of us. . . .

When the President had finished, Edison rose and said:

> This experience makes me realize as never before that Americans are sentimental, and this crowning event of Light's Golden Jubilee fills me with gratitude. As to Henry Ford, words are inadequate to express my feelings. I can only say to you that in the fullest and richest meaning of the term—he is my friend. Good night.

White-faced, Edison slumped into his seat. To some in the hall it seemed as if he were dead or dying. Hastily, Mrs. Edison had him taken to a room behind the dais, where the presidential physician revived him with drugs. He was put to bed at the Ford residence and remained there for several days.

Light's Golden Jubilee had duly been celebrated. "I am tired of glory," the old inventor said. "I want to get back to work."

8

one

A World
Without
Electricity

THE last great festival of the pre-electrical era was the World's
Fair of 1876, held in Philadelphia to commemorate the hundredth anniversary of our nation's independence. The Centennial Exposition was intended as a summary of the Republic's
first century, a recapitulation of ten decades of progress and expansion. Therefore, naturally, it placed heavy emphasis on
industrial development.

The fairgoers who visited the wonderland at Fairmount Park
could view such things as 50-ton locomotives, gas stoves, George
Westinghouse's air brake for railway trains, and ingenious devices for making everything from shoes to buttonholes. The most
striking exhibit stood in the center of Machinery Hall: a pair of
giant 1400-horsepower steam engines, designed by George H.
Corliss, rearing 30 feet high like a brace of captive dinosaurs.
These mighty and monstrous engines seemed to be the embodiment of power in metal, for from the broad pistons and huge
boilers came an unbelievable output of mechanical energy.
Surely the Corliss titans were the wonders of the age. It was
little more than a century since James Watt had patented his
first small steam engines, so in a sense the Philadelphia fair

marked not only the national anniversary but the anniversary of the era of steam power.

The exposition displayed less spectacular-looking but equally inspiring inventions. On opening day Emperor Dom Pedro II of Brazil stood by the exhibit of Alexander Graham Bell and put the newly invented telephone to his ear. "My God, it talks!" the monarch cried in surprise. The telephone was an electrical device, but it was operated by battery power; there was no other kind of current readily available. Of course, machines had been constructed that could generate electricity. They were called dynamos, and two of them were shown at the fair—one Belgian, one American. Each was hooked up to power an electrical arc lamp, which produced a dazzling bluish light as current leaped across a gap between two carbon rods. The bright, sputtering flare of light was an interesting curiosity that attracted many viewers, and sent them away blinking and rubbing their eyes. One of the electrical exhibitors had a second dynamo that drove a small pump. But the future prospects of electrical power seemed modest indeed under the same roof with the Corliss steam engines. While the arc lamps were fascinating oddities, the buildings of the fair were nevertheless illuminated by the gentle glow of gaslight.

A young inventor named Thomas Edison, twenty-nine years old, showed two of his recent successes at the exposition. They were both in the field of telegraphy, where he had won fame and early fortune. One was his multiplex telegraph, a revolutionary instrument that permitted the transmission of four simultaneous messages over a single line. The other was an automatic telegraph that made use of perforated paper tape to send messages six times as fast as the fastest human telegrapher.

The telegraph, too, was an electrical device. Unlike the telephone, it had been in use for a generation and had reached an advanced state of technical perfection, largely due to the efforts of young Edison. For its power requirements, which were small, batteries were sufficient. In 1876 it held a vital place in the nation's communication system. Soon the telegraph would be forced aside by Bell's telephone; and soon the Corliss steam engine would go to join the dinosaurs in extinction, because Edison would offer a far more efficient source of power. But the triumph of the telephone seemed unlikely in 1876, and the triumph of electricity was even more remote. Not even Edison himself then imagined how deeply he would involve himself with that mysterious, invisible, intangible force in a few more years.

The telegraph aside, it was still a pre-electrical era. The horsecar was the chief means of transportation. Each city had its many stables, its thousands of busy horses, its population of grooms and blacksmiths and buggy salesmen. Rich men had their own carriages; common folk rode the horsecars, which were warmed in winter by wood or coal stoves. New York City, always in the vanguard of things, soon would have in addition several elevated lines of trains drawn by steam locomotives, with long flat pans under the engines to keep ashes and hot water from spilling through to the street.

Steam was the prime mover of industry. Forced into a movable cylinder, steam caused a piston to rise; when a condenser cooled the steam, the piston fell back. James Watt had shown how to transform the reciprocating motion of the piston into the revolving motion of a shaft, and all during the nineteenth century others had struggled to improve the steam engine's low efficiency. Most of the steam's energy still was dissipated without performing any work, but enough was harnessed to drive all sorts of machinery. Boilers hissed, pistons clattered, shafts whirled, belts went endlessly round and round, and the nation grew wealthy.

The towers of Manhattan, some of them six stories high, were served by steam-powered elevators. The elevators were hydraulic, rising on columns of liquid that extended into the ground to a depth equal to the height the elevator was to travel. Steam en-

11

gines ran the pumps that created the pressure to lift the cars, and the exhaust steam of the engines provided heat for the buildings in winter. No large building was without its bulky, towering, window-rattling steam engine. And horse-drawn carts bearing coal to feed the boilers plodded constantly through the streets.

As darkness fell, the lamplighters emerged. Gaslight, a daring and awesome innovation when it first came to New York in 1825, now was universal in the land. Smoky, odorous oil lamps had long ago vanished from the streets. The lamplighters, many of them limping veterans of the Civil War, made nightly rounds to kindle the small yellow glows, although thrifty cities often had the gas lamps extinguished on moonlit nights. Indoors, the prosperous citizens lit their homes with gas mantles, while those who did not subscribe to the gas company's costly service made do with kerosene lamps or tallow candles. The smell of burning fuel was ever-present; hardly anyone noticed it.

Bicycles were new and startling. Steamships still were rarities. Railroad tracks spanned the nation, but the journey to California was interminable, and anywhere west of Missouri the trains were subject to Indian attack. Millions of shaggy brown bison roamed the plains. It was the year of Custer's Last Stand and the heyday of Buffalo Bill.

Rutherford B. Hayes and Samuel J. Tilden campaigned for the presidency that year without benefit of radio, television, air transport, voting machines—or telephone, since the only telephones then in existence were in the workshop of Alexander Graham Bell. In the chaotic conditions accompanying the political re-entry of the South into the Union, disputed elections resulted. News traveled so slowly that the nation had a difficult time following the complex turn of events. And it took months for the politicians, traveling back and forth by train and horse-car, to deal with the situation and determine the identity of the incoming president.

A few far-sighted men were investigating electricity in 1876.

Several recent technical developments had made it feasible to generate electricity in quantity, using mechanical means—the dynamo—rather than chemical means—the battery. There was talk of establishing companies to provide arc light service in the streets of several American cities. These electrical pioneers included such men as Charles F. Brush, Edwin J. Houston, Elihu Thomson, William Wallace. They were all earnest, hard-working men with a strong grasp of electrical theory, such as it was (and it was not very much) in the 1870's. None of them had the true spark of genius, though.

That spark burned brightly in Thomas Alva Edison, whose startling career was already well under way. Edison had set himself up in business in 1869, at the age of twenty-two, as the prototype of the free-lance professional inventor. By the time of the 1876 exposition, he had won considerable commercial success, had been awarded more patents than any six other men, and was highly regarded both by technically-minded men and by the Wall Street captains who were financing the new epoch of industrial growth. He was interested in the phenomenon of electricity, of course, and had done some sketchy work with arc lights and batteries as early as 1875. But at the moment he had other, more immediately profitable projects to deal with. For the time being, Edison left electrical research to Brush, Houston, and the rest.

What was this stuff *electricity*, anyway?

Certainly no one could have given a coherent answer to that question in 1876. Today we can supply a variety of statements, more or less accurate. But on close analysis it turns out that most of what we can say about electricity really describes what it *does*, not what it *is*.

The ancients saw electricity flash across the sky as lightning: to them it was the thunderbolt of Zeus, the hammer of Thor. They knew that certain stones had the power of attracting metal. Thales of Miletus wrote two thousand five hundred years ago, "All things are full of gods. The magnet is alive, for it has the power of moving iron." But they did not know the connection between the magnetism in a lodestone and the lightning leaping through a stormy sky.

Men played with magnets, and in time found a practical use for them as compasses to show the poles of the earth. The earth itself was a great magnet, it seemed, which could make a magnetic needle point north and south. The puzzle of magnetism consumed the energies of many men, without great results, until Sir William Gilbert, court physician to Queen Elizabeth I, studied the known magnetic materials, and went on to test a few more. He found that amber, which the Greeks called *elektron*, became magnetic when rubbed with a soft cloth. From this Gilbert concluded that there must be some magnetic force that passes into certain materials—a force he called the *vis electrica;* amber, iron, copper, and many other substances contained the *vis electrica.*

Gilbert and later experimenters found that it was possible to build up a charge of the *vis electrica* (which became known as "electricity") through friction. Rubbing a glass rod with silk, for example, gave the rod an electric charge. A comb could be charged by drawing it through one's hair. Once charged, these substances acted the way natural magnets did; the charged glass rod could pick up little bits of paper exactly as a chunk of magnetic lodestone would draw loose nails to itself.

Through friction, then, it was possible to create an electric charge in certain substances—and that electric charge induced a magnetic field. Also, Gilbert noticed, the electric charge might sometimes be discharged all at once, in the form of a spark, when a charged object was placed near an uncharged one.

Often a charged object would repel instead of attract. This led to the notion that there were two types of electrical charge, one "positive" and one "negative." Objects carrying a positive charge tended to attract negatively charged objects, and to repel other positively charged ones. The chief author of this concept was Benjamin Franklin, one of the most devoted of the early electrical experimenters. It was Franklin's famous kite experiment, in 1752, that proved that lightning was nothing more than a great electrical discharge, a magnified form of the tiny electrical spark that could be seen leaping from a charged object to an uncharged one in the laboratory.

A great deal was known, by Franklin's time, about generating electricity by means of friction. As early as 1650, Otto von Guericke, the mayor of the German town of Magdeburg, had built a crude friction generator—a sulfur ball that rotated at high speed on a shaft. When Guericke held his hand against the ball and turned the shaft rapidly, a charge built up. The electricity thus generated, Guericke noticed, could be transmitted along a length of linen thread to charge a second sulfur ball.

Soon improved models of the Guericke machine were in use, employing glass globes or plates instead of sulfur, and drawing off the electricity with metal forks. In 1745 another German, Ewald Georg von Kleist, found a method of "bottling" the electricity thus produced. Kleist lined a glass jar with silver foil, and charged the foil with his friction machine. Quite a satisfactory charge was collected, as Kleist discovered when he touched the wires running from the bottle and received a vehement shock. A year later, Pieter van Musschenbroek of Leyden independently performed the same experiment and was surprised when an unsuspecting friend, handling the apparatus, suffered a staggering shock. Musschenbroek repeated the experiment on himself with similar result, declaring that he "would not take another shock for the kingdom of France." Since he and not Kleist was the one to make the storage jar known to the scientific world, it was dubbed the "Leyden jar."

Friction machines and Leyden jars became commonplace toys of scientifically-inclined eighteenth-century gentlemen.

One of them discovered that electricity could be carried at least four miles over a copper wire. Another found a chemical application for the current, producing water by sending a spark through a mixture of hydrogen and air. But no one could see any practical use for the new force. There was no way of generating it in quantity, nor could the spark discharges be controlled to any great extent.

In 1792 the Italian physicist Alessandro Volta observed that two dissimilar metals, placed in contact with a fluid that conducted electricity, displayed a difference in electrical potential between them. This difference could best be expressed in terms of electromotive force, whose unit measure—the *volt*—today bears Volta's name. After eight years of work, Volta assembled a workable "pile," or battery, consisting of alternating pairs of silver and zinc disks with flannel disks separating each metallic pair. When the pile was soaked in brine and the top disk of zinc was connected to the lowest disk of silver by a wire, an electric current flowed through the wire.

Volta's battery at last provided a dependable—if limited—source of electricity, and the more disk pairs, or cells, that were added to it, the greater the voltage produced. The English chemist Sir Humphry Davy experimented with the Voltaic battery about 1802, and noted that he could heat thin strips of metal to white heat by passing a current through them. He had come upon the basic principle of the incandescent light; but Davy's strips glowed for only a moment before they oxidized in the atmosphere and burned up.

It was Davy who, in 1809, discovered an alternate method of getting light from electricity—the arc light. Using a Voltaic battery of 2000 cells, he ran a strong current through two carbon rods whose tips were only a short distance apart. The arc of electricity leaping from one rod to the other created a brilliant blue-white light. However, the carbon rods were quickly consumed. Nor was there any practical way of generating large quantities of electricity, suitable for extensive lighting, with the Voltaic battery.

Both the tinkerers and the theoreticians continued to work, but for a long time it was only the theory that showed any gains. In 1820 the Danish scientist Hans Christian Oersted observed that the electric current from a battery produced magnetic effects. He showed clearly what men had been groping toward since William Gilbert's day: that a conductor carrying electricity is surrounded by a magnetic field. Two months after Oersted's work was published, André Marie Ampère of Paris expanded on it by demonstrating the interaction of electric currents and magnets. Ampère's theoretical work led to the immediate development of the first electromagnet: a steel needle that was magnetized by placing it within a coil of wire carrying a current. His name was immortalized in the unit of electric current: the *ampere*.

Magnetism thus could be produced by electricity. Could the operation be reversed, and electricity be produced by magnetism? Ampère decided it could not. But in 1822 a former bookbinder's apprentice named Michael Faraday jotted in his notebook, "Convert magnetism into electricity," and set about doing it.

Faraday had risen from lower-class obscurity to become the most brilliant pupil of the great Sir Humphry Davy. In 1813, when he was twenty-two years old, Faraday had accompanied Davy on a tour of Europe and had met Ampère and Volta. Soon Faraday was a luminary of science in his own right. Between 1822 and 1831 he repeatedly attacked the problem of electromagnetic induction, and on his fifth attempt he succeeded in perfecting the first modern dynamo.

Faraday built his work on the foundation laid for him by Oersted, Ampère, and the Frenchman D. J. F. Arago, who in 1825 had rotated a flat disk of copper beneath a magnetic needle, causing the needle to follow the rotating disk. On August 29, 1831, Faraday made his first significant discovery. He wound two coils of wire on opposite sides of an iron ring, insulating them from one another and from the ring. Then he sent current from a battery through one coil, magnetizing it. Instruments attached to the second coil did not show the presence of any electric current in it. But when he connected or disconnected the battery and the first coil, a momentary current was produced in the second coil.

He grasped the principle: a *change* in the magnetic field of the first coil induced an electric current in the second one.

Faraday now took a cylindrical bar magnet three quarters of an inch thick and eight and one half inches long, and thrust it into a spiral coil of copper wire. When the magnet entered the coil, electric current flowed in the wire; as the magnet was removed, current flowed in the opposite direction. But when the magnet was allowed to remain motionless in the coil, there was no current. Electricity could be produced from a magnet, but continuous motion was necessary. Faraday reasoned: the current came from the constant cutting of what he called "lines of magnetic force."

Using a horseshoe magnet, Faraday rigged a means of rotating a flat copper disk between its poles. As the disk moved it constantly cut the magnetic field between the poles of the magnet, producing a steady flow of current. As Faraday put it, "If a terminated wire moves so as to cut a magnetic curve, a power is called into action which tends to urge an electric current through it."

Faraday could not say *why* the constant cutting of a magnetic field should induce an electric current. It remained for the brilliant James Clerk Maxwell, a generation later, to demonstrate mathematically the relationship between electricity and magnetism. Yet Faraday knew the vast potential importance of his discovery. It promised to yield electricity in a quantity far beyond the capacity of friction machines or Voltaic batteries.

Among the visitors to Faraday's laboratory about that time was William Gladstone, then Chancellor of the Exchequer. Gladstone watched Faraday's simple dynamo for a while and finally asked, "But, after all, what good is it?" Faraday replied, "Why, sir, one day you will tax it."

But Faraday had no interest in the commercial exploitation of his invention. He did not even bother to patent it. He was willing to leave the practical application of electricity to others, declaring, "I have rather been desirous of discovering new facts and new relations dependent on magneto-electric induction, than of exalting the force of those already obtained; being assured that the latter would find their full development hereafter."

Had Faraday shown an Edison-like interest in going from the theoretical to the practical, the electrical age might well have arrived thirty or forty years sooner than it did. For indeed it was not until the decade after Faraday's death in 1867 that the would-be developers of electricity made any important progress toward large-scale use of the electromagnetic dynamo. Until then, the Voltaic battery remained the chief source of electricity, too feeble to produce anything but a weak current. Battery current was sufficient to operate the electric telegraph, which Samuel F. B. Morse perfected in 1844 after some years of work. But batteries could not provide the power to run machines, nor could they supply current to light streets and homes.

Before there could be electric light and power, there had to be a reliable generator. Faraday's little machine was only a prototype. Swiftly, though, other men were in the field, making use of the theoretical knowledge so generously bestowed upon them by Faraday. In 1832, Hippolyte Pixii exhibited in Paris an electrical generator in which the magnet revolved and the coils remained stationary. It was hand-driven, so its electrical output was a function of the strength and endurance of its operator. Built-in inefficiency limited the effectiveness of Pixii's magnetic

19

field, too. He wound his conductive wire on long spools, hoping in that way to crowd a maximum amount of wire into a minimum of space, but then arranged his spools so that they were parallel to the bars of the rotating horseshoe magnet. An ideal generator would have had the coils at right angles to the magnetic field; in Pixii's machine, only a small amount of his coil was actually cutting the lines of magnetic force.

The Pixii generator produced alternating current: the field of the rotating magnet was cut first in one direction, then in the other, as the horseshoe turned, producing a cycle of interrupted pulses of electricity. This was regarded as a drawback, but Ampère showed Pixii how to modify his device to produce direct current, as Voltaic batteries did. Ampère suggested the use of a *commutator*, a rotating switch that reversed the connection between the wound coils and the outside circuit every time the current changed direction.

An American, Joseph Saxton, built a similar generator in 1833. It also had a pair of spool-wound coils, but they rotated past the poles of a fixed horseshoe magnet—the opposite of the Pixii arrangement. Saxton's use of moving coils and stationary magnet was generally adopted by his successors.

By a process of trial and error, many men worked toward a satisfactory electromagnetic generator. A commercial motivation appeared when a popular fad led to the use of electricity for therapeutic purposes. A mild shock was thought to be beneficial to health. To meet the demand, a considerable quantity of hand-driven generators was manufactured on both sides of the Atlantic, and in the course of this work certain modifications in generator design developed. The advent of commercial electroplating and electrotyping in 1839 gave even greater impetus to generator construction. Electricity was no longer an experimenter's plaything; it was becoming a business.

The generators of the 1840's represented only small steps forward from the Saxton generator. Gradually, more efficient placement of the spinning coils appeared, as well as the use of more effective magnets and groups of magnets. About 1850, a Frenchman named Nollet built a generator in which a number of coils rotated past the poles of several horseshoe magnets, providing a relatively large electrical output. Nollet planned to use the power to illuminate a lighthouse, employing the recently invented "limelight" technique in which intense light was produced by heating a block of lime to incandescence. Little came of the scheme.

An Englishman, Frederick Hale Holmes, patented improvements on the Nollet generator in 1856. Holmes's generator, which won the enthusiastic approval of Faraday, weighed 4,000 pounds and consisted of 36 rotating horseshoe magnets and a number of large iron cores, or armatures, on which the conducting coils were wound. It produced some 1500 watts of power, impressive for its time.* Holmes's bulky machine was driven by a steam engine, and thus was one of the earliest examples of a generator that converted the mechanical energy of steam into electrical energy.

All generators so far had relied on permanent magnets, though the more efficient electromagnet had been known for some thirty years. In 1855 a Dane named Søren Hjorth patented a generator that incorporated an electromagnet. In the early models, current was supplied to the electromagnet by batteries or by small auxiliary generators. (An electromagnet, which is a combination of coiled wire and an iron core, produces a magnetic field only when a current passes through it.) Soon the principle of the self-exciting generator became apparent. A small degree of residual magnetism in the iron core of the electromagnet sufficed to provide the initial field; the field increased in strength as the generator's output built up and some of the current thus generated was fed back to the electro-

* The watt, the basic unit of power, is defined electrically as a current of one ampere moving at a force of one volt. Wattage equals amperage times voltage.

magnet. Start-up batteries and auxiliary generators could be discarded.

Improvements in coil design followed this important improvement of the magnet. In 1856, E. W. von Siemens of Germany devised the "H" or "shuttle" armature, which permitted a greater speed of operation. Later he combined his new armature with a self-exciting electromagnet. In 1867, this sort of generator received the name by which it was popularly known for many years—the dynamo. (The term was the coinage of one Charles Brooke, who referred to machines that converted mechanical energy into electrical energy as "dynamo-electric." An electric motor, capable of converting electrical energy back into mechanical energy, was an "electro-dynamic" machine in Brooke's terminology. "Dynamo-electric" was quickly shortened to *dynamo*.) Since the early generators were largely of the direct-current type, the word dynamo was reserved for such machines; the later alternating-current generators became known as *alternators*.

The Siemens armature turned out to pose practical problems. In 1860 an alternative was proposed by Antonio Pacinotti, professor of physics at the University of Pisa. Pacinotti discarded the standard spool-shaped armature and wound his coil on an iron ring. The Pacinotti armature revolved in the plane of the lines of force between two electromagnets, and the ring winding presented a greater amount of the coil to the magnetic field than did the spool winding. Pacinotti published his work in an Italian theoretical journal; the idea, attracting little attention, rapidly dropped from sight.

It was rediscovered in 1870 by Zénobe Théophile Gramme, a Belgian living in Paris. Gramme's dynamo had the same ring-wound principle as Pacinotti's. A steam engine rotated the armature, which was made of soft iron wire about which coils of copper wire were wound. Unlike Pacinotti, Gramme found eager businessmen to finance the production of his dynamo. It was really the first electrical generator that yielded a satisfactory amount of continuous current with any degree of efficiency, and it was quickly adopted for such electrical needs as had appeared, mainly electroplating, lighthouse illumination, and outdoor arc lighting. The availability of the Gramme dynamo in the early 1870's caused a considerable boom in all those activities.

The dynamo had not quite reached its final form, though. The ring-wound armature wasted much of its effectiveness, because the inner portion of the coil generated no useful current. From Germany in 1872 came F. von Hefner Alteneck's drum armature, in which there was no inner winding at all. The armature consisted of a wooden drum on whose outer surface the coils were placed. This allowed a much greater length of wire to perform the necessary perpendicular cutting of the magnetic field.

The Hefner Alteneck dynamo offered new technical problems at first: such things as overheating of the armature windings and excessive sparking at the commutator brushes. Many years would pass before the full merit of the drum armature could be realized, and in those years the Gramme dynamo reached widespread acceptance.

It was an age of steam, however, and though the half century from Faraday to Gramme had seen slow but steady progress toward a cheap and plentiful supply of electricity, no one yet thought very seriously about replacing steam engines with electric motors. An electric motor would be essentially a dynamo operating in reverse, converting electricity into a magnetic field that would cause the shaft of the motor to move and perform work. Until there was a reasonably efficient dynamo, there could hardly be a remotely efficient electric motor; so the electrical engineers of the pre-Edison era concentrated not on electrical applications for power but for light.

They had two routes to follow, both of them pioneered in the first decade of the nineteenth century by Sir Humphry Davy:

23

that of the incandescent light and of the arc light. Of the two, the incandescent light seemed more attractive for general use, but the technical difficulties were formidable.

An electrical current, passing through a conductive substance, generates some degree of heat. Certain substances, upon application of a powerful enough current, grow so hot that they glow. This is the principle of incandescence. Unfortunately, it was readily apparent that anything hot enough to incandesce is also hot enough to burn up in the atmosphere in short order.

Putting the incandescent substance in a vacuum was one way around that problem. In 1820 a French experimenter mounted a coil of platinum wire in a glass tube, pumped out as much of the air as possible, and sent a battery-generated current through the coil. Since he could achieve only a partial vacuum, the wire quickly burned out. His task was compounded by his use of platinum, a metal in which the temperature of incandescence is very close to the melting point. And with batteries the only source of current, there was no practical hope of any immediate public use for incandescent lights.

In 1840, while the early dynamo-builders were getting under way, Sir William Robert Grove began his approach to the problem of electric lights by conceiving a better battery. The Grove battery had a voltage of 1.9 volts, nearly double that of previous batteries, and with it Sir William powered an incandescent lamp at a demonstration for the Royal Society. He used a coil of platinum wire mounted at the ends of insulated copper wires that were in turn connected to his battery. The apparatus rested in a shallow glass vessel partly filled with water, and was covered by an inverted tumbler to protect it from drafts of air. It burned only a short while.

W. E. Staite, another Englishman, used an alloy of platinum and iridium, with only modest success, about the same time. His countryman Frederick De Moleyns obtained the first patent on an incandescent lamp in 1841, using a different method. He employed two platinum coils set a short distance apart, with powdered charcoal bridging the gap between them. The charcoal became incandescent when the current was turned on. De Moleyns' lamp, like Staite's, was no more than a passing novelty, suitable only for exhibit at scientific meetings and lectures.

At one of Staite's demonstration lectures, given in October, 1847, a nineteen-year-old chemist named Joseph Swan watched in fascination as the little lamp produced its ephemeral glow. Swan was a country boy, who had not even had a Londoner's advantage of dwelling in a gas-lit city. As he wrote many years later,

> The days of my youth extend backwards to the dark ages, for I was born when the rushlight, the tallow dip or solitary blaze of the hearth were the common means of indoor lighting. . . . In the chambers of the great, the wax candle, or exceptionally a multiplicity of them, relieved the gloom on state occasions; but as a rule, the common people, wanting the inducement of indoor brightness such as we enjoy, went to bed soon after sunset.

To Swan, electricity held forth hope of a brighter world, and soon he found himself gripped by an obsession with incandescence. Checking the technical literature, he uncovered a patent of 1845, filed on behalf of one J. W. Starr of Cincinnati. Starr claimed having applied "continuous metallic and carbon conductors, intensely heated by the passage of a current of electricity, to the purposes of illumination." A thin sheet of carbon enclosed in a vacuum had apparently been Starr's most successful technique for producing light.

Starr, it turned out, had died in 1847. Swan commenced his own work the following year by attempting to master the unexpectedly difficult technique of making strong and flexible strips of carbonized paper. After twelve years of work, he was able to fashion fairly good incandescent lamps that used carbon

25

strips one quarter of an inch wide and one and one half inches long. Then he realized that his labor was futile; vacuum technology was still too primitive to allow adequate exhaustion of air from the bulb, so the lamps were of necessity short-lived. With the Gramme dynamo still a decade in the future, there was no acceptable source of current other than batteries. In 1860 Swan dropped his work on incandescence and did not pick it up for seventeen years.

Meanwhile an American, Moses Farmer of Massachusetts, had achieved history of sorts in 1859, as the first to use electricity for residential lighting. Farmer lit the parlor of his Salem home with incandescents, using strips of platinum in open air, and drawing the current from batteries. But the idea clearly had no practical value, and Farmer abandoned it in favor of designing dynamos.

In Russia, an inventor named Lodyguine tried to sidestep the problem of obtaining a vacuum by filling the bulb with an inert gas, such as nitrogen. Using a V-shaped graphite burner that was protected from oxidation by a shroud of gas, Lodyguine did develop a passable incandescent light, and in 1874 received a $25,000 award from the Russian Academy of Sciences for his work. Some two hundred Lodyguine lamps were installed in the Admiralty Dockyard at St. Petersburg, but they proved too expensive for practical use.

The vacuum method became more feasible after 1865, when Hermann Sprengel invented the mercury vacuum pump. A decade later, Sir William Crookes was evacuating glass tubes, not to use for incandescent lights but to investigate the mysterious radiation produced when he sent a current through a vacuum. Crookes had taken the first uncertain step toward the discovery of the X-ray and the electron.

When Joseph Swan heard of Crookes's work, he was drawn once more to the old dream of incandescence, and, in 1877, resumed his interrupted research. Thanks to Sprengel's pump and Gramme's dynamo, there was now some hope of success, where in 1860 there had been none. He placed a carbon rod within an evacuated glass bulb and passed a current through it. It glowed, but still deteriorated quickly. When he demonstrated a relatively successful incandescent lamp in December, 1878, he had to admit that he was far from being ready to offer a workable commercial light.

By that time, Thomas Edison had entered the field. His preliminary survey of the state of the art had shown him that no one, not even Swan, was on the right track. When Edison began his work on the incandescent light, it was inaugurated with a breathtaking disregard of his predecessors' achievements. Only the basic principle of incandescence was the same; his goals and methods were unique.

two

The Man
Who Invented
Almost
Everything

EDISON came along too late to invent the telegraph, so he had to be content with improving it. Another man beat him to the telephone, though Edison went on to build a better one. He might have given us radio, but he overlooked a vital clue. He was busy with other things when the automobile and the airplane were developed.

Those were the inventions that Thomas Alva Edison never got around to making. Nearly all the rest of our modern technological miracles sprang from the fertile brain of this cantankerous, determined, wholly improbable genius. The list is awesome: the phonograph; the telephone transmitter; motion pictures; multiplex telegraphy; the electric storage battery; the mimeograph machine; the automatic telegraph; the stock ticker; and dozens of other inventions great and small that flowed from his least obvious and most abstract invention, the industrial research laboratory.

The incandescent light bulb, for which he was honored so exhaustingly at Dearborn in 1929, was only a small part of his contribution to the electrification of the world. He saw as a coherent whole, and devised, an entire system of electric distribution, carrying power from central stations to light fixtures in the home. Not one invention but dozens constituted the Edison electrical accomplishment. He produced a magnificent constellation of interrelated achievements: dynamos, power lines, cables, switches, sockets, junction boxes, wires, insulators, meters, fuses, connectors, conductors, manhole boxes, chandeliers, methods of interior wiring, voltage regulators, bulbs, and scores of other devices. Ordinary men might spend their lives puzzling over how to make a dynamo or a lamp, but Edison created an industry. From his dusty laboratory at Menlo Park sprang the fundamental energy source on which modern progress is based. Edison, in seeking to give the world light, also opened the way to cyclotrons and toasters, to radio and television, to electric typewriters and electric toothbrushes, to tape recorders and electric shavers, to electrified trains, loudspeakers, thermostats, sparkplugs, traffic lights, elevators, computers, pumps, smelters, refrigerators, air conditioners, washing machines, night baseball games, and much, much more. As thirty million Americans discovered during the startling power failure of November 9, 1965, when the electricity stops, the world stops.

Any one of Edison's major achievements—the incandescent bulb, the phonograph, the motion picture—would have been a creditable life's work for an inventor. Edison's restless mind, though, turned from one enterprise to another in an endless quest for mastery in a dozen fields. If he had chosen to retain and exploit all his patents, he could have built a personal fortune to dwarf that of John D. Rockefeller. Money for Edison, however, was merely the means to finance new experiments; he sold his interest in one company to pay for the research expenses of the next. Although he died a wealthy man, he forfeited his chance to be a billionaire in order to carry on continued investigation.

Born in that now inconceivably remote era of buggies and

gaslight, Edison transformed the world about him, and lived long enough to ponder the problem of harnessing and using atomic energy. His father, Sam Edison, was a Canadian. Tall and powerful in build, he was by trade a carpenter, by choice an insurrectionist. Sam Edison's departure from Canada came abruptly in 1837, upon the failure of a movement to overthrow the Royal Canadian Government. Legging it eighty miles through frozen woods, he crossed an ice-covered river into the United States, which he adopted as his new homeland. This sort of turbulence was traditional in the Edison family; the inventor's grandfather, John Edison of New Jersey, was a prosperous Tory who opposed the American Revolution and took up arms against George Washington's militiamen in 1776. Convicted of high treason by New Jersey's Council of Safety, John Edison was sentenced to be hanged, but at the last moment was spared and went into exile in Canada. There he sired a host of sons, the rebellious Sam Edison among them.

Thomas Alva Edison joined this unruly line on a snowy February night in 1847, in Milan, Ohio. He was the seventh of seven children, a frail, fair-haired infant whose head seemed abnormally large. The boy showed early promise of living up to the example of his individualistic father and grandfather. At the age of six he set a fire in Sam Edison's barn, "just to see what it would do," and received a public parental thrashing in the village square. That failed to deter him from making further experiments—of all sorts—though there were no more barn fires.

Dreamy and difficult, he had few friends, did poorly in school, and struck his family and neighbors as an eccentric, dull-witted child. Only his mother seemed to sense the potential strength of his mind, and nurtured him on a diet of Shakespeare, Dickens, and Gibbon's *Decline and Fall of the Roman Empire*. When Tom was nine, she offered him an elementary science text, Parker's *School of Natural Philosophy,* which described chemical experiments that could be performed at home. It lit a blaze in young Edison that glowed for the next seventy-five years.

The boy set up a home laboratory in a corner of the cellar. Noxious odors filled the house, and occasionally there was the muffled sound of a small explosion. Hoping to carry Benjamin Franklin's work with electricity a stage further, Tom wired the tails of two tomcats together and vigorously rubbed their fur. This yielded no current but got him some bloody scratches. "Thomas Alva never had any boyhood days," his father once observed. "His early amusements were steam engines and mechanical forces."

The boy's obstreperous curiosity both delighted and irritated adults. He would ask question after blunt question, until his victim was reduced to replying, "I don't know." And then Tom would demand: *"Why* don't you know?"

The elder Edison was usually in financial difficulties, and his son took odd jobs in order to pay for the materials he needed in his experiments. The summer he was eleven Tom raised several hundred dollars, by growing and marketing vegetables, and ploughed the money into his latest interest—telegraphy. The telegraph, Samuel F. B. Morse's handiwork, was new and exciting, the biggest advance in communications since the domestication of the carrier pigeon. Edison and a friend built their own crude telegraph, running a house-to-house line through the trees and insulating it with the necks of bottles. Far into the night they tapped messages to one another. Gradually the network of telegraph lines spread through the neighborhood, and Edison, who had some instinctive facility with Morse code, often chafed with impatience when his friends were unable to follow his high-speed transmissions. The local telegraph system ended catastrophically. A stray cow wandered

31

into the Edison yard one night, knocked down a pole carrying the wires, and soon became so entangled that she pulled down most of the surrounding poles. Her mournful mooings brought helpful neighbors who cut her free, but that was the end of Edison's telegraph line.

In 1859, at the age of twelve, he concluded his formal education and went to work as a "candy butcher" on the new Grand Trunk Railway line. The Edison family now lived in Port Huron, Michigan, one of the terminals for the line. A train left Port Huron at seven each morning, reached Detroit about three hours later, remained there loading freight most of the day, and puffed back to Port Huron at 9:30 P.M. On this dawn-to-midnight schedule Edison peddled newspapers, sandwiches, and candy. Because he had no duties during the long daily layover in Detroit, he hatched the idea of installing his cellar laboratory in the baggage car, and using his free time for experiments. The trainman agreed, and the test-tubes, batteries, and bottles came aboard.

A famous (but probably apocryphal) story about Edison has it that one day some chemicals caught fire aboard the train, causing the conductor to toss the twelve-year-old experimenter out the door at the next stop, laboratory and all. Supposedly a printing press that Edison had added to the laboratory was also thrown from the train. And, the story goes on, the angry conductor boxed the boy chemist's ears so severely that lifelong deafness resulted.

It is a pathetic, picturesque tale, with a kind of Dickensian charm, but it never happened that way—as Edison often tried to make clear. The haphazard jumbling of the sequence of events by a careless nineteenth-century biographer created this particular myth. There was a fire, yes—in 1862, when Edison was nearly fifteen. The conductor did ask Edison to remove his laboratory from the train after a sudden violent lurch ignited some phosphorus and set the wooden baggage car ablaze; but there was no ear-boxing and no rude dumping overboard. The printing press did not even come aboard the train until some months after the incident of the fire. As for Edison's deafness, it began two years before the fire, when he was thirteen. Edison later explained, "I was trying to climb into the freight car with both arms full of heavy bundles of papers. . . . I ran after it and caught the rear step, hardly able to lift myself. A trainman reached over and grabbed me by the ears and lifted me. . . . I felt something snap inside my head, and the deafness started from that time and has progressed ever since." (Scarlet fever some years earlier may also have affected his hearing.)

Edison's deafness further cut him off from the companionship of those about him, and forced him to rely on inner resources. "I haven't heard a bird sing since I was twelve years old," he wrote sadly in his diary many years later. He plunged deep into a campaign of self-education, devouring books in wholesale lots, now Victor Hugo, now Isaac Newton, now Burton's *Anatomy of Melancholy*, now Karl Fresenius' *Chemical Analysis*. Burton's ponderous essay struck him as "pretty heavy reading for a youngster," but he pushed through it. Newton's *Principia* was a "wilderness of mathematics" to him, though, and after hours of effort he abandoned it. He declared later, "It gave me a distaste for mathematics from which I have never recovered."

Still supporting himself with his train job, he dabbled in printing, publishing a small newspaper to be peddled on the train. This remarkable enterprise, the *Weekly Herald*, was strictly a one-man operation; Edison wrote all the copy, set it in type himself during idle hours on the train, ran it off on a small secondhand press he had purchased with his savings, and hawked the paper at the substantial price of three cents a copy, eight cents a month, from car to car.

At the height of its success the *Weekly Herald* had a regular circulation of about five hundred. Travelers who frequently made the Detroit-Port Huron run were amused by the boy publisher's ingenuity and persistence, but they also found his paper useful. In it Edison published such things as timetable changes not otherwise easily available, and, when he could obtain them, late news flashes from telegraph operators at stations along the route. Today only one copy of the *Weekly Herald* survives, the edition of February 3, 1862, which was somehow preserved and hangs framed in the palatial Edison mansion in West Orange, New Jersey. It is a single large sheet, printed on both sides. Spelling and grammar are on the wayward side, as might be expected from a fifteen-year-old of limited formal education, but the typography is commendable and the grasp of journalistic technique is such that it is clear to see the newspapers of Edison's day lost a great reporter when he turned to inventing.

In the lone surviving edition Edison editorially praises one of the Grand Trunk Railway's engineers, offers a suggestion for the hiring of an extra porter at each station, and tells in detail of a thwarted attempt to bilk the company of the value of an allegedly lost suitcase. There are military notes—appropriate enough in 1862—and a variety of timetable announcements and stagecoach schedules. Fillers include the information that "The thousandth birthday of the Empire of Russia will be celebrated at Novgorod in august" and the somber reflection, "Reason Justice and Equity, never had weight enough on the face of the earth to govern the councils of men." For light relief Edison attempted such sallies as, " 'Let me collect myself,' as the man said when he was blown up by a powder mill." Classified advertisements occupied part of the second page, and there were such market notes as these:

> Butter at 10 to 12 cents per lb.
>
> Eggs at 12 cents per dozen.
>
> Lard at 7 to 9 cents per lb.
>
> Dressed hogs at 3.00 to 3.25 per 100 lbs.
>
> Mutton at 4 to 5 cents per lb.

Those prices, of course, reflected the severe wartime inflation of the day.

Edison's profit on the *Weekly Herald* came to something like $45 a month, but he put himself out of business by growing too ambitious. A newspaperman friend of his persuaded him to turn the *Herald* into a gossip sheet called *Paul Pry*, and sell it in Port Huron. The new paper was uninhibited and outspoken in its candidness, causing the central figure of one of its stories to track Edison down, seize him by the seat of his pants, and toss him into the St. Clair River near the Port Huron docks. With that, *Paul Pry* ceased publication.

Its proprietor's interest in telegraphy was reviving, anyway, so perhaps the newspaper died a natural death as Edison moved to other fields. Once again he and a friend rigged a neighborhood telegraph line, this one running half a mile. Somehow deafness was an advantage to him in telegraphy, for he was able to hear the clicking of the instrument undistracted by surrounding noises. In the late summer of 1862 Edison stepped from amateur to professional telegraphy. He was waiting at the Mt. Clemens station of the Grand Trunk line when the three-year-old son of the stationmaster toddled into the path of an oncoming train. Edison snatched the boy to safety, and the grateful father, who was an experienced telegrapher, offered to reward him by teaching him the secrets of his trade.

Edison was coming to think that selling candy on a train held little future for him, now that he was past fifteen. So the solemn, rather undersized boy, giving up his train job, commenced telegraphy lessons. He showed up the first day bearing a neat set of telegraph instruments that he had made himself from bits of scrap. Boarding with the stationmaster, Edison spent five months learning to send and receive messages the professional way. By then he knew as much about the art as his teacher did, so the stationmaster suggested that he apply for a job as night operator at the Port Huron station. He got the post—at a salary of $25 a month.

The duties were not very arduous. About all he had to do was record the passing of trains and relay messages to other stations down the line. He had ample time to leaf through back copies of the *Scientific American,* to toy with electrical circuits of his own design, or to improve his technique by cutting in on despatches coming to the local newspaper.

Soon Edison joined the ranks of the wandering telegraph operators, a gypsy-like tribe of young men who worked in one place only long enough to earn the money they needed to move on to another. May of 1864 saw him employed as a railroad despatcher at Stratford Junction, Ontario, about forty miles from Port Huron. Here he worked from 7 P.M. to 7 A.M., handling messages and confirming arrivals and departures.

The trains ran sparsely, and Edison sometimes had trouble remaining awake through the long, dull nights—particularly since he failed to sleep, as a night worker should, during the day. He tried to take cat naps between trains, hoping to awaken in time to send the acknowledging signal, but that was clearly a risky business. Furthermore, the Grand Trunk Railway had a rule that each station operator had to signal the main office at certain hours during the night, simply to show that he was awake.

Edison's check-in signals always arrived punctually—except once. When the telegrapher in the main office replied to the signal, he got no answer. Some checking explained the mystery. The new operator at Stratford Junction had put together a clockwork mechanism which automatically, at the proper check-in hours, flashed the signal to the main office. If Edison dozed past the hour, no one would be the wiser. It did not, however, provide for answering a return signal.

It was Edison's first real invention, but it won him no praise, merely a stinging reprimand for his misplaced cleverness. He continued to take brief naps on the job—it was a habit he maintained all his life—but now, instead of relying on mechanical deception, he arranged for a night yardman to awaken him periodically. This worked well until the night that the yardman was late. The horrified Edison awoke to see a train leaving the station, and a moment later the telegraph chattered out an order for him to hold that very train! He replied that it was too late, that the train had already gone through. Back came the chilling news that another train only a station away was coming up the same track in the expectation that Edison had shunted the first train onto a siding.

A head-on collison seemed imminent. Edison rushed out and down the track in a futile attempt to catch the train he had let slip by. In the darkness, he dropped into a gully and was knocked unconscious. When he came to, he learned that the engineers, approaching disaster in ignorance, had seen each other's lights in time to avoid a smash. A badly frightened and guilty Edison chose to resign the next morning, and quietly slipped back into the United States to look for a new job.

His seventeenth birthday in 1864 marked the outset of a nomadic year. He went to Toledo, then to Fort Wayne, where all he could find was a daytime job, not to his liking. By autumn he was on Western Union's payroll in Indianapolis at $75 a month. The following February he drifted along to Cincinnati. He had great technical skill as a telegraph operator, sending and receiving at a furious pace. More than that, Edison showed a keen interest in the fundamental working of the device. He began to produce innovations of his own, such as a gadget for recording messages as they came in. It was an ingenious invention, particularly for a boy in his late teens, but he had difficulty persuading his supervisors to use it.

He had difficulty keeping jobs, too. Self-centered, over-imaginative, unwilling to accept discipline, Edison saw himself as a giant held down by pygmies, but the pygmies kept firing him. His fondness for practical jokes did not enhance his employability; once, bothered by fellow operators who forgot to put the office water dipper back beside the common pail, he wired it to a battery so that anyone lifting it would get a mild shock.

His salary was consumed in purchasing scientific texts and electrical equipment, and he spent his days experimenting before reporting for his nighttime jobs. There was little left over for food, rent, or clothing, but Edison was indifferent then and always to matters of personal comfort or appearance. So long as he had a room, however vermin-infested, and so long as he had a meal whenever he felt hungry, there was no need for more elaborate arrangements.

He was in Cincinnati on the night of April 14, 1865. As he told the story later,

> I noticed an immense crowd gathering in the street outside a newspaper office. I called the attention of the other operators to the crowd and we sent a messenger boy out to find the cause of the excitement. He returned in a few minutes and shouted, "Lincoln's shot!" Instinctively the operators looked from one face to the other to see which man had received the news. All the faces were blank and every man said he had not taken a word about the shooting. "Look over your files," said the boss to the man handling the press stuff. For a few minutes we waited in suspense, and then the man held up a sheet of paper containing a short account of the shooting of the President. The operator had worked so mechanically that he had handled the news without the slightest knowledge of its significance.

Edison himself had cultivated the same capacity for concentration on the job at hand; it was a quality he never lost.

Milton Adams, one of the other telegraphers in the Cincinnati office, described the Edison of that year as

> decidedly unprepossessing in dress, and rather uncouth in manner. . . . His nose was very prominent, giving a Napoleonic look to his face. . . . As an operator he had no superiors,

38

and very few equals. Most of the time he was "monkeying" with batteries and circuits. He arranged in the cellar what he called his "rat paralyzer," a very simple contrivance, consisting of two plates insulated from each other and connected with a main battery. They were so placed that when a rat passed over, the fore feet on the one plate and the hind feet on the other completed the circuit and the rat departed this life electrocuted.

For a while Edison enjoyed close friendship with Adams, a slightly older and far more sophisticated man. Then telegraphers' wanderlust overcame them; Adams headed for Boston, Edison to Memphis. He came into the Memphis Western Union office, another friend wrote, wearing "a hickory shirt, a pair of butternut pants tucked into the tops of boots a size too large for him and guiltless of blacking. 'Where's the boss?' was his query, as he glanced around the office."

Edison's bumptious manners inspired the other telegraphers to play a prank on him. They assigned him to handle the St. Louis wire, and the St. Louis operator was famous for his rapid-fire sending. Tipped off in advance, the St. Louis man began to blaze a message in as fast as he could. One witness wrote,

> Edison threw his leg over the arm of the chair, leisurely transferred a wad of spruce gum from his pocket to his mouth, took up a pen, examined it critically, and started in about fifty words behind. He didn't stay there long, though. St. Louis let out another link of speed and still another, and the instrument on Edison's table hummed like an old-style Singer sewing-machine. Every man in the office left his desk and gathered around to see what he was doing with that electric cyclone. Well, sir, he was right on the word and taking it down in the prettiest copperplate hand you ever saw, even crossing his "t's" and dotting his "i's" and punctuating with as much care as a man editing telegraph for rat printers. St. Louis got tired by and by and began to slow down. Then Edison opened the key and said, "Hello, there! When are you going to get a hustle on?"

39

Soon he was recognized as the fastest operator on the Western Union system. That gave him prestige in the office, but the moment he got away from his telegraph instrument he was lost. Sensitive, awkward, tortured by his deafness, conscious of his great potential ability but unable to put it to use, Edison spent a harrowing adolescence. His uncouth ways and burning inner drives made him an uncomfortable companion, and his fellow telegraphers generally left him alone after hours. He seemed to prefer solitude, because there was so much he wanted to read and so many experiments he wanted to try, but there were painful moments when the loneliness broke through.

After a quarrel with the Memphis office manager Edison moved on to Louisville, where he remained more than a year. His offhours gadgeteering, random and unfocused until then, now took on a definite objective. He sought to devise a duplex telegraph—one that would allow the transmission of two simultaneous messages over a single wire. Such a telegraph would instantly double the capacity of Western Union's lines, and he saw the invention as the gateway to fame. Feverishly he toyed with the wiring and batteries in the Louisville office, seeking some clue toward a duplex method. As usual, the office manager was angered by the ambitions of the would-be inventor, and ordered Edison to leave the equipment alone. Edison persevered secretly. As he told his biographer forty years later,

> I went one night into the battery-room to obtain some sulphuric acid for experimenting. The carboy tipped over, the acid ran out, went through the ceiling to the manager's room below, and ate up his desk and all the carpet. The next morning I was summoned before him and told that the company wanted operators, not experimenters.

Edison dropped his duplex work, and soon after, a Boston inventor named J. B. Stearns took out a patent for a duplex apparatus. Edison always felt that the hostility of the Louisville manager was all that had kept him from making the great discovery first.

Restless and ambitious, he came now to see that he had little future as an organization man. If only he could obtain a sizable sum of money in some dramatic coup, he thought, he would have the leisure to devote himself to invention. Word came to him early in 1867 that the government of Brazil was offering high salaries to experienced telegraphers who would aid in constructing telegraph networks through the Brazilian jungle. From this Edison concocted a romantic fantasy of building a telegraph empire in the valley of the Amazon. He began to teach himself Spanish—evidently unaware that the language of Brazil is Portuguese—and booked passage on a steamer soon to sail from New Orleans.

With two other telegraphers he journeyed to New Orleans only to find the city under martial law after recent riots against a "carpetbagger" reconstructionist administration. In the chaos, departure of the steamer was delayed just long enough for Edison to meet a Spaniard who had lived in Brazil and to learn from him the nature of the dangers and privations that lay in wait there. Edison prudently abandoned the project and returned to Louisville. His two friends sailed anyway, getting no farther than Mexico, where they died of yellow fever.

Louisville held no more excitement for him now than it had before. Late in 1867 Edison resigned again and went home to Port Huron for a family visit. There he found a letter from Milton Adams, his friend of Cincinnati days, singing the praises of life in Boston. Edison wrote back to ask Adams if Western Union had an opening for another operator there. "Come along," Adams replied. "There's a big chance for you here and I will get you a job."

Boston, the "hub of culture," was America's most exciting city. To Boston, then, went Tom Edison, journeyman telegrapher, in quest of fortune.

three

Free-Lance
Inventor

EDISON wangled a pass from his old employer, the Grand Trunk Railway, and set out by train from Port Huron to Boston via Montreal in March, 1868. He was a month past his twenty-first birthday and thus far had given the world little clue that he was destined for greatness.

Blizzards delayed him on his journey. He arrived in Boston fatigued and ragged, a hayseed of hayseeds with long hair, baggy clothes, a wide-brimmed hat, a plug of tobacco between his teeth. He seemed almost deliberately to cultivate an air of bumpkinhood. But in five minutes he demonstrated his formidable telegraphic competence to the local Western Union manager, and he had a job.

Predictably, the other operators in the office put him through a hazing that had become tiresomely familiar by now. The fastest man on the New York line was instructed to put him to the test. Edison responded as he had in Memphis, taking down the sizzling copy and boredly telling his adversary, "Say, young man, change off and send with your other foot." He enlivened office life by building an electrified cockroach-killer patterned after his Cincinnati "rat paralyzer." He loaded his boardinghouse bedroom with telegraphic paraphernalia and second-hand textbooks.

One of the prizes he secured in a Cornhill bookshop was a set of Faraday's two-volume classic, *Experimental Researches in Electricity*. In Faraday he felt he had found a kindred spirit, a man who probed the mysteries of the universe not by scratching calculations on a sheet of paper, but by building machines and making them work. The night he brought the Faraday books home, Edison began reading at four in the morning and continued well into the day. The clear prose, the revelation of exciting possibilities, the sense of dedicated questing—these things drew Edison's deepest sympathies. "His explanations were simple," Edison later wrote. "He used no mathematics. He was the master experimenter. I don't think there were many copies of Faraday's works sold in those days. The only people who did anything in electricity were the telegraphers and the opticians, making simple school apparatus to demonstrate the principles."

Through Edison's mind whirled the image of Faraday's copper disk, a foot in diameter, cutting across lines of magnetic force to generate electricity. He saw the collecting brushes that carried off the current; he contemplated the mounting of the magnet; he followed breathlessly every detail of Faraday's work, and lost no time repeating the master's experiments himself. Though he did not know it, he was not far from the workshop of Moses Farmer, the only American who was seriously concerned with dynamo technology at that time. It seemed to Edison that he alone had any interest in electricity's great possibilities, though he knew in a vague way that certain Germans and Frenchmen had been working on machines to generate current after Faraday's principles. Faraday became Edison's deity. To Milton Adams he said breathlessly, "I am now twenty-one. I may live to be fifty. Can I get as much done as he did? I have got so much to do and life is so short that I am going to hustle."

His nights were at the service of Western Union; his days were spent touring the shops of Boston's manufacturers of telegraphic and electrical instruments. He met Stearns, the man who had beat him to the duplex telegraph. He struck up a friendship with Charles Williams, Jr., in whose small shop all sorts of experiments were encouraged, and was given a corner of the place for himself. At the Williams place he investigated the interesting explosive compound known as dynamite, perfected only the year before by the Swedish scientist Alfred Nobel. A very small quantity of dynamite produced "such terrific and unexpected results that we became alarmed," Edison wrote, "the fact dawning on us that we had a very large white elephant in our possession. At 6 A.M. I put the explosive into a sarsaparilla bottle, tied a string to it, wrapped it in paper and let it gently down into the sewer, corner of State and Washington Streets."

There were other excitements. Pulling a battery from a shelf, he sustained such burns and stains from spilling acid that he kept off the streets by daylight for two weeks. He claimed—too optimistically—to have achieved a major improvement in the duplex transmission system, and Milton Adams promptly dashed off a premature article for *The Journal of the Telegraph,* hailing the new young genius.

At the Western Union office his boredom expressed itself in such a variety of pranks that his superiors let it be known that his resignation would be welcomed.

Edison obliged. Nor did he make application for a job at some other Western Union branch. Henceforth he would be his own master. In January of 1869 he placed an announcement in a trade journal to the effect that Thomas A. Edison "would hereafter devote his full time to bringing out his inventions." He offered models of his "double transmitter" for sale at $400 and noted that he could be found at Charles Williams' shop on Court Street.

It was a bold venture. He had no capital, little business experience, no assets but his surging ambition. But by the time he took the big step into self-employment he had already produced his first patentable invention: a telegraphic vote-recording machine.

It seemed to Edison that the clumsy legislative method of totalling ayes and nays was a tedious waste of time. He persuaded an office friend named Roberts to invest $100 in the development costs, and used his niche in the Williams shop to assemble a working model of his vote-counter. This ancestor of all voting machines consisted of a roll of chemically treated paper inserted in a printing device. Legislators at their desks would have two buttons, one for aye, one for nay; when they pressed one, a telegraphic impulse was transmitted to the counter at the front of the chamber, where the vote was instantly recorded on the paper. There would be no delays in reaching a total, nor was chicanery possible.

Edison applied for his patent in October, 1868. It was granted on June 1, 1869: patent number 90,646 for the United States, patent number 1 for Thomas Alva Edison. So beautiful, so logical was the device that Edison was convinced his fortune was made. Every state and municipal legislature, even Congress itself, must surely desire such a mechanism! Hours would be saved through the elimination of dreary roll-calls, while the much-abused voice vote would become extinct.

On borrowed money Edison went to Washington to offer his vote-counter to Congress. With difficulty he gained an interview with a committee of Congressmen and demonstrated his equipment. It functioned perfectly. He waited to hear that an immediate order would be placed. Instead, a row of chilly faces confronted him, and one of the legislators declared,

> Young man, it works all right and couldn't be better. With an instrument like that it would be difficult to monkey with the vote if you wanted to. But it won't do. In fact, it's the last thing on earth that we want here. Filibustering and delay in the counting of the votes are often the only means

we have for defeating bad legislation. So, though I admire your genius and the spirit which prompted you to invent so excellent a machine, we shan't require it here. Take the thing away.

It was an instructively disillusioning experience. Edison's admiration of Faraday had led him to combine that great scientist's idealistic abhorrence of practicality with a Yankee determination to profit by cleverness. But it was not a workable combination. One could devote oneself to purely theoretical work, or one could try to earn a living by devising inventions to order; one could not do both at once. "Of course I was very sorry," said Edison afterwards, "for I had banked on that machine bringing me in money. But it was a lesson to me. There and then I made a vow that I would never invent anything which was not wanted, or which was not necessary to the community at large. And so far I believe I have kept that vow."

He looked about for some more profitable way to capitalize on his knowledge of telegraphy, and was drawn toward the stock ticker. It was a period of frenzied speculation, both in common stocks and in gold (which was openly traded on the commodity markets, as copper and wheat and soybeans are today). An active financial market required up-to-the-minute information on price fluctuations, and in 1866 a broker named S. S. Laws had invented a telegraphic gold indicator. This telegraphic device relayed price changes from the floor of the Gold Exchange to subscribing brokerage houses in the financial district in New York.

Boston, too, had a thriving market in stocks and gold. In 1867 a Boston inventor named E. A. Callahan had gone Laws one better by producing what he called a "stock ticker," from the sound it made. This was also a telegraphic instrument whose battery-powered type-wheel printed out stock market quotations as well as gold prices on a moving paper tape. A company called the Gold & Stock Telegraph Company was formed to utilize the Callahan ticker, and soon won many subscribers in Boston, as well as competing successfully with Laws's Gold Indicator Company in New York.

The Callahan ticker, though, required the presence of a special attendant on the receiving end in the office of each subscriber, and demanded vast quantities of costly wiring. Edison studied its defects for a while, and in January of 1869 applied for a patent on a modified version. A company was formed to use the Edison ticker in Boston. Soon it had some thirty subscribers. But the unwary inventor failed to safeguard his patent rights. His backers speedily took full control of the invention, and he was left with nothing to show for his work but his newly gained experience and confidence.

He had already formed the habit of working on as many things at once as possible; so, while developing the vote-counter and the stock ticker, he was also deep in an improved duplex telegraph system. It seemed to him that Stearns's duplex scheme, which Western Union was then trying out on an experimental basis, was considerably less than ideal. In the spring of 1869 Edison found a Bostonian named Welch to put up cash for developmental work, in exchange for a half interest "in any instrument or method which I may invent to be held for the transmission of messages on telegraph lines both ways simultaneously." He poured all of his own savings into the project as well.

Shortly he had an experimental model of a duplex transmitter. Apparently it was not notably different from Stearns's device, for Edison filed no patent application on it. He offered to demonstrate it at the Boston office of Western Union, but met with no interest there. Since Western Union had not then achieved its monopoly of the telegraph business, Edison quickly turned to a rival company, the Atlantic & Pacific Telegraph Company, which consented to permit Edison to show his instrument.

He was invited to set up his duplexer at the Rochester, New York office of the company and send trial messages to the New York City office, four hundred miles away. Going still further in debt, Edison scraped up the cash needed to transport his equipment from Boston to Rochester and readied himself for the demonstration. He arrived on a Saturday, waited until early Sunday morning for clear wires, and began to signal New York. There was no response. What the reason was Edison did not know, but he was unable to make contact. After several unhappy days of further trials, he abandoned the effort and bleakly returned to Boston.

He was in a dismal state. Of his three 1869 inventions, one had misfired, one had failed to find a buyer, and one had been snatched from him by the unscrupulous. He had no money and his credit in Boston had been impaired by the duplexing fiasco. Last year he had been known there as a bright young man worth watching; this year he was a failed genius at twenty-two. What now? Well, there was New York, bigger and wealthier than Boston, the financial if not the cultural capital of the nation. He could make a new start there.

Increasing his already heavy debts by a few dollars, Edison borrowed enough to buy a ticket on the night boat to New York. He left all his possessions behind—his instruments and tools, his books, his technical magazines. Penniless, baggageless, he stared at the metropolis of New York by the light of a spring dawn and pondered, like millions before him had done and millions yet unborn would do, ways of winning the great city's attention.

His beginning was inauspicious. There was only one person in New York that he knew, and that person was not at home. So Edison spent his first day and his first night in New York walking the streets. He wangled a free cup of tea at a warehouse far downtown, where a newly arrived cargo of tea leaves from Ceylon was being tasted; then he stopped into a telegraph office and borrowed a dollar from a friendly operator with which he bought a meal of apple dumplings and coffee.

Next he called at the office of S. S. Laws's Gold Indicator Company. He met there Franklin L. Pope, an electrical engineer, who knew of Edison's own stock ticker work in Boston. Pope saw advantages in befriending the young wanderer, and invited Edison to share his office. Edison could use the machine shop of Gold Indicator for his experiments, and could sleep on a cot in the company's cellar battery room until he had found a place to live. He passed the next two or three nights there; during the daytime, he examined the Laws indicator and mastered its workings.

The frantic gold speculation of June, 1869 was keeping Wall Street busy and the tickers humming. Soon after Edison's arrival came one of the wildest trading days yet, for Jay Gould, Jim Fisk, and other buccaneers were surreptitiously laying the groundwork for a gaudy market raid in gold. Suddenly the central stock ticker that was sending out the gold quotations broke down. All over the financial district brokers, shouting that their machines had failed, erupted into the streets. Edison happened to be in the office at the moment. Pope and the other company engineers panicked, bustling about the machine in such agitation that they were unable to detect the cause of the trouble. Now Laws himself appeared, faced with the ruin of his company if he could not restore reliable service at once.

"Fix it! Fix it!" Laws yelled. "Be quick, for God's sake!"

Edison stepped forward. With difficulty he gained the attention of the flustered Pope and the vehement Laws and pointed out the difficulty: a contact spring had broken off and dropped between two gear wheels. Since no one else seemed calm enough to do what had to be done, Edison plucked forth the broken spring, replaced it, and set the indicator dial back to zero. Within two hours the gold quotations once more were being transmitted. Like the plucky hero of a dime novel, Edison had saved the day.

Laws hired him on the spot as Pope's assistant. A month later, Pope left to start his own engineering firm, and his job went to Edison at an opulent salary of $300 a month. Edison would have preferred to remain a free-lance, but he was realistic enough to see at this juncture that he needed to rebuild his meager capital first.

All that summer he ran the indicator capably, keeping it from breaking down and demonstrating ways to improve the mechanism. His most severe test came on September 24, 1869, "Black Friday," when Gould and Fisk attempted to corner the gold market and stand the national economy on its head. As they made their well-timed moves, the price of gold leaped upward in unprecedented bounds. The perspiring Edison labored to keep the indicator in touch with the price fluctuations, but the machine was slow, and he fell far behind. The panic in Wall Street raged all day as Gould and Fisk played out their strategy. Said Edison long afterwards,

> I sat on top of the Western Union telegraph booth to watch the surging, crazy crowd. One man came to the booth, grabbed a pencil, and attempted to write a message to Boston. The first stroke went clear off the blank. . . . Amid great excitement Speyer, the banker, went crazy and it took five men to hold him; and everybody lost their head. The Western Union operator came to me and said, "Shake, Edison, we are O.K. We haven't a cent." I felt happy because we were poor. These occasions are very enjoyable to a poor man; but they occur rarely.

Late in the day, the United States Treasury countered the raid by dumping gold reserves onto the open market. Now the price of gold began to fall, and Edison again struggled with the indicator. When news circulated that the manipulators had casually repudiated the purchase contracts they had executed in

50

the morning, the market broke altogether. For Edison, it was an education into the ways of high finance that served him well. Although he would be intimately involved with the moneymen in years to come, he would never let himself become a party to their desperate gambles.

Six days after that memorable Friday, Edison was in business for himself again. The decision was not altogether voluntary. The Gold Indicator Company's chief competitor, Gold & Stock Telegraph (which used the Callahan ticker), was bought out by Western Union. Rather than compete against that giant corporation, Laws chose to sell out too. In a grand consolidation the two financial quotation firms became subsidiaries of Western Union. Edison had no enthusiasm for becoming a Western Union employee again, and he politely declined when General Marshall Lefferts, the head of the new combined ticker company, asked him to stay on.

Instead Edison went into partnership with his friend Franklin Pope. The October 1, 1869 issue of *The Telegrapher* ran a half-page advertisement proclaiming the formation of what actually was the United States' first firm of professional consulting electrical engineers:

> Pope, Edison & Co.—Electrical Engineers and General Telegraph Agency—Office, Exchange Buildings, Nos. 78 and 80 Broadway, Room 48.

Edison boarded at Pope's home in Elizabeth, New Jersey, thus beginning a lifelong attachment to that state. They rose at 6 A.M. each morning and caught the 7 A.M. train to New York, passing the day there meeting customers and stirring up new work. At 6 P.M. they crossed the Hudson to Jersey City, where they rented a small shop near the railway station, and carried out the work they had contracted in New York. Usually they worked in the shop until about 1 A.M., when they returned to Elizabeth to catch a few hours of sleep before beginning the cycle again. It was no pleasant routine, especially when winter arrived, but Edison thrived on such rigors.

Western Union stood ready to buy up any invention that might threaten its communications monopoly; so the chief endeavor of Pope, Edison & Co. was to turn out devices that Western Union would feel impelled to buy. Edison contrived a new version of the stock ticker that used small relay magnets and an electrically driven escapement, similar to that in a clock, to drive the printing wheel. He and Pope announced that they were prepared to supply quotations at a low weekly rental of $25. Instantly Western Union stepped in, buying the rights to the ticker for $15,000. Of this Edison received only $5,000. He and Pope had taken on a silent partner, J. L. Ashley, publisher of *The Telegrapher,* who contributed no capital to the partnership, donating advertising space in his publication in lieu of cash. There were several further transactions in which, though Edison had done most of the work, he received only a third of the proceeds. So in the summer of 1870 Edison amicably severed the partnership. "I got tired," he said, "of doing all the work with compensation narrowed down to the point of extinguishment by the superior business abilities of my partners."

Edison by now had an extensive collection of patents on stock ticker improvements, but the balky device still had its flaws. Western Union asked him to work on the Callahan machine and cure it of its occasional habit of going berserk and spewing out streams of erratic figures. In three weeks Edison had a model to demonstrate. He brought it to General Lefferts' office and put it through its paces with great success. Typically, he had not troubled to negotiate a fee before undertaking the work. Now, Lefferts asked him how much he wanted for the rights to his new ticker.

Edison considered that $5000 would be about right, but he was prepared to have Lefferts bargain him down to $3000 or so. As he liked to tell the story in later years, he hesitated to ask for any such sum, and blurted, "General, suppose you make me an offer."

"How would $40,000 strike you?" Lefferts asked.

The startled Edison collected himself and admitted that he was willing to do business at that figure. A contract was drawn, and Lefferts handed him a check three days later. It was the first check Edison had ever received, and he had only a faint notion of how to go about cashing it. After some misadventures at the teller's window, he came away with a foot-thick stack of $10 and $20 bills. Bewildered, he stuffed the money into his pockets, drew a loose overcoat about him, and hurriedly boarded the ferry for New Jersey, where he sat up all night in his room—he was now living in a Newark boardinghouse—guarding his hoard against imaginary thieves. In the morning he bundled the cash up and took it back to New York, where General Lefferts explained that it might be simpler if he deposited the money in a bank.

His stock-ticker prosperity gave him the opening he needed. Western Union asked for 1,200 of the improved tickers, to be produced over a period of several years—an order amounting to nearly half a million dollars. Edison rented a Newark loft, turned it into a machine shop, and soon was employing 18 men. He wrote to his parents, "I am now what 'you' Democrats call a 'Bloated Eastern Manufacturer.'"

Surrounding himself with a capable staff of assistants, most of them older than he was, Edison at twenty-four became a mass producer of inventions. Chiefly they were refinements on the original system of telegraphy, and so he found himself ensnared willy-nilly in the patent wars between the mighty Western Union and its many ephemeral competitors of the day. Having acquired his shrewdness the hard way, he became adept at business dealings, always minimizing his risks and insuring himself of a fair return for his work. He was unwilling to let himself be devoured by such financial sharks as Jay Gould and Commodore

Cornelius Vanderbilt, then engaged in a seesaw war for control of Western Union. By selling his patents outright or accepting a royalty basis, rather than attempting to maintain full control, he kept his involvement in their machinations at a minimum. Even so, he spent nearly as much time in court defending his patent rights as in his laboratory.

The patents mounted. He was in his natural element, with all catastrophes seemingly behind him and the incomparable stimulus of steady success to keep him soaring ever higher. The prolific inventor was awarded 38 patents in 1872, and 25 more the next year, for such things as telegraph printers, relay magnets, and stock-ticker modifications. By 1876 he had received more than 200 patents, but he was only warming up. In 1882 alone Edison filed 141 patent applications.

Teamwork was the method by which he achieved these formidable results. The Edison laboratory was unique in its many-minded approach to technical problems. Inventing was a profession for loners when Edison took it up, but he changed that. His workshop at Newark, and its successors at Menlo Park and West Orange, New Jersey, were the ancestors in spirit of such mighty industrial research laboratories as those of today's Bell System and General Electric. Which is not to say that Edison leaned unduly on the minds of other men. The real fountain of ideas was always his own imagination, and no one worked longer hours or contributed more to the overall result.

In those busy early years at Newark Edison began assembling the capable team that figured in many of his later achievements. His assistant foreman was John Ott, who had come to him in 1870 when he still had the shop in Jersey City. Edison had confronted the twenty-one-year-old Ott with the heaped-up parts of a disassembled stock ticker and asked, "Can you make this machine go?"

"You needn't pay me if I don't," said Ott, and put it together.

54

He was Edison's chief draftsman in years to come, taking the inventor's rough sketches and turning them into superb diagrams. The job of transforming Ott's diagrams into working models generally fell to Charles Batchelor, who became Edison's "hands." This black-bearded Englishman was first sent to the United States to install special machinery at a sewing mill in Newark. He visited Edison's new factory nearby, became fascinated by what was being done there, and presented himself for employment. The indefatigable Batchelor found no mechanical work too delicate or too taxing.

Heavier machine-making became the province of a Swiss clockmaker named John Kruesi, whose gift for constructing devices of unusual form was extraordinary. Another member of the original Edison team was a German, Sigmund Bergmann, with a rare capacity for hard work and skillful production. Edison was the conceiver, the sketcher, the initiator; it remained for Ott, Batchelor, Kruesi, and Bergmann to execute his ideas.

The factory grew. Soon he employed 50 men, and ran a night shift. Then the work force reached 250. Young Edison now presided over what was becoming a large industrial organization; but he still ran it in hit-or-miss fashion, keeping the books according to his own haphazard ideas, working an irregular schedule that might find him putting in sixty consecutive hours at the laboratory and then declaring a holiday, and moving from project to project in happy impetuosity. At one time he was working at 45 inventions at once in the Newark shop.

To keep track of all this he began to make entries in a daily notebook. In large folio volumes he set down day-by-day records of his experiments, along with sketches of machines drawn in his own hand. Each page was dated, and each was witnessed by three assistants, who initialed each drawing and every important paragraph. The first of these daybooks was begun at Newark on July 28, 1871, with the notation, "This will be a daily record containing ideas previously formed, some of which have been tried, some that have been sketched and described, and some that have never been sketched, tried or described." Edison kept the notebook up to date for nearly thirty-five years, and it became an invaluable collection of documentary evidence for use in later patent trials, as well as a revealing display of his remarkable career. Beside most of the entries Edison added later evaluations of the work in his own terse code: "N.G." for "no good," "L.B." for "little better," "E." for "encouraging," "V.E." for "very encouraging," and so forth. One crisp sentence in an early entry sounds a vigorous declaration of independence: "Invented by & for myself and not for any small-brained capitalist."

The small-brained capitalists, though, stood by to purchase the rights to each Edison wonder as it emerged. Often they brought the crippled inventions of other men to him for repairs. One day in 1871 a young engineer named Edward H. Johnson appeared in Newark bearing a model of a new kind of automatic telegraph for Edison to examine. It made use of moving paper tape to transmit and receive messages at high speed. At close range it worked well, but beyond two hundred miles it printed its messages slowly and blurrily. Edison, who had invented an automatic telegraph of his own during his gypsy-telegrapher days, rapidly saw what was wrong with the machine and what had to be done to perfect it. Johnson had been sent by the newly incorporated Automatic Telegraph Company, reputedly the agent by which the sinister Jay Gould hoped to destroy Western Union, and Edison accepted a $40,000 contract to produce a workable high-speed automatic telegraph for the new company. As part of the deal, he insisted that Edward Johnson work with him "for the duration of the project." That began a fruitful association that would last more than twenty years.

Not that it took Edison twenty years to get the automatic telegraph working properly. By the winter of 1872 he was testing a device that transmitted a thousand words a minute between New York and Philadelphia. He patented it that August, and, by the terms of his agreement, assigned the patent to Automatic Telegraph. But the machine merely printed the message out in dots and dashes; it still had to be decoded at the receiving end. It occurred to Edison to mate his stock ticker and his automatic telegraph, yielding a machine that would type out messages automatically in Roman characters. This enterprise occupied him during the early months of 1873. In one hundred and twenty nights of testing he created a working model. It seemed certain that Western Union would totter before the unbeatable advantage Edison's machine would give Automatic Telegraph.

Then Jay Gould stepped forward, openly acknowledged his control of Automatic Telegraph, and took charge of the company. Edison became aware that his patents were in the hands of Wall Street's most rapacious operator. Gould had no real interest in improving telegraph service, or indeed in improving anything but the state of his own bank balances. He intended to use Edison's automatic telegraph only as a weapon in his campaign to seize control of Western Union.

Edison found himself on both sides in that campaign, for while developing his automatic telegraph for Gould's company, he had at the same time been producing impressive improvements in telegraph technology for Western Union. The challenge of sending more than one telegraph message on a single line, which had obsessed him since adolescence, had now been successfully met.

Early in 1873, Edison had visited William Orton, president of Western Union, to announce that he could build a duplex telegraph better than the Stearns duplex then in use. "He treated the business of making the duplex as a very trifling affair," Orton said later. Orton commissioned him to work on it, giving him the use of Western Union's wires for his experiments. Stearns's duplex could send two messages on one wire only in opposite directions; Edison proposed to employ certain characteristics of electrical current to send *two messages in the same direction*.

57

This, said Orton, would be a great boon, since, "as with street-cars, everybody wants to go downtown in the morning and uptown at night."

By the spring of 1873 Edison was successful with his duplex, and he applied for a patent on April 23. Then he went off to England to discuss the licensing of some of his inventions by the British government. When he returned he found a financial panic going on in Wall Street. Stocks were down, money was tight, Orton refused to see him, and Western Union did not care to invest further cash in the duplex. Edison himself felt the pinch, and avoided bankruptcy only by intense juggling of accounts.

Edison had a new idea to offer Western Union, not merely a duplex but a quadruplex telegraph. For if he could send two messages one way on a wire—and he could—why not send two more simultaneously in the other direction? But without financial support he could not proceed with the quadruplex, so he put the idea aside and concentrated on the automatic telegraph.

Early in 1874 the rival telegraph companies staged a dramatic contest. President Grant was delivering an important message of some eleven thousand words; and Automatic Telegraph arranged to transmit it from Washington to New York over a single wire, using Edison's printing device. Ten clerks punched the paper tape recording the Presidential message; two operators ran the automatic sender; and thirteen copyists took the message down as it arrived in New York. The whole process took just sixty-nine minutes. But at the same time Western Union, using Edison-designed equipment over eight lines, got the message to New York in only one minute more, employing just sixteen men altogether.

Telegraph competition had never been sharper. Orton once more offered to back Edison, and by the summer of 1874 a workable quadruplex was ready to be patented. Orton delayed outrageously in giving Edison any money; the inventor, strapped for cash and bent under the burden of high development costs, finally took his quadruplex over to Jay Gould's company, at the beginning of 1875. This caused an immediate catastrophic drop in Western Union's stock, and also launched a bitter and intricate patent suit for the rights to use Edison's invention.

Though he was only a pawn in the bewildering events that followed, Edison had gained at least one benefit: he was now famous. Singlehandedly he had brought forth a revolution in telegraph communications with his automatic machine and his astonishing quadruplex, and everyone knew it. From the board rooms of Wall Street to the classrooms of Main Street, the name of Thomas Edison was becoming a household word.

Gould's name was legendary, too, for different reasons, and he proceeded to live up to his reputation. First, early in 1875, he merged Automatic Telegraph into another of his companies, the Atlantic & Pacific Telegraph Company. Edison was promised a payment in Atlantic & Pacific stock for his services, but through some fast bookkeeping he received nothing. (Edison sued; the case dragged on until 1906, by which time Gould was dead and Edison no longer needed the money.) Then, with a stranglehold on all the key patents, Gould brought Western Union to surrender and merged it with his own Atlantic & Pacific. Until his death in 1892, Gould was absolute monarch over the new Western Union, with its near-monopoly of telegraph communications. Having achieved his kingdom, he had no further interest in paying cash for technical improvements, and in fact discarded many of Edison's inventions, among them the automatic telegraph. Until jolted by the success of the telephone, Western Union was content to stand pat. "When Gould got the Western Union," said Edison, "I knew no further progress in telegraphy was possible, and I went into other lines."

four

The Wizard of
Menlo Park

EDISON'S Newark years had been rewarding and exciting ones. He had established himself firmly as the most fertile technical mind of the era; he had risen from obscurity to national fame; and he had made a great deal of money, although nearly all of it had passed through his hands without sticking. From Jay Gould he had learned a simple lesson: don't deal with Jay Gould. From Western Union of the pre-Gould era he had learned how to cope with giant corporations without being ruined. The years from 1870 to 1876 had been a fiery baptism for the young inventor, but he had come through the blaze with his self-confidence unimpaired and his prospects splendid.

For all his long hours at the laboratory, he had even found time to take a wife. Edison had fallen in love with one of his own shop workers, sixteen-year-old Mary Stilwell, and they were married in 1871. A family tradition says that Edison headed for his workshop right after the ceremony and toiled far into the night to repair some malfunctioning stock tickers, while his puzzled bride awaited his return in unhappy solitude. Finally an associate entered the laboratory and found Edison there.

"What time is it?" Edison asked him.

"Midnight!"

The inventor shook his head. "Midnight? Is that so? I must go home then—I was married today."

Mary Edison was gentle, simple, a girl of no particular education, who revered her dynamic husband and gave him a free rein. No doubt she was largely a neglected wife, more of a pet than a companion for the inventor, whom he left to her house and her babies while he put in his sixteen-hour and eighteen-hour working days.

The flow of inventions was boundless. Among his minor inventions was a telegraphic burglar alarm, which he sold outright to the Automatic Telegraph Company. He produced an electric pen, motor-operated, which perforated a sheet of paper to form a stencil that could be used to run off many copies. This was perhaps the first time a small electric motor had been manufactured and sold in large quantities. (The power was supplied by batteries.) The electric pen of 1874 led the following year to a "device for multiplying copies of letters" that used wax-coated stencils. It was the mimeograph, an invention that few connect with Edison today because he lost interest in it and sold his rights to A. B. Dick of Chicago. A by-product of this work was paraffin-coated paper, used for wrapping food products and also rarely associated with Edison.

By 1875 Edison had come to be dissatisfied with the Newark operation. He was attempting to carry two loads at once—to be an inventor and to run a manufacturing venture. The Newark factory turned out a variety of products, most of them small and unprofitable, and supervising this activity required a disproportionate amount of Edison's time. What he wanted to do was get out of manufacturing entirely, retire to some quiet country retreat, and devote himself exclusively to inventing. His income would come from properly executed licensing arrangements with large corporations. No longer would he have to worry about landlords, the cost of labor, the headaches of invoices and shipping, or any of the other problems that had beset him as a conventional businessman. It was back to the original concept of the Pope, Edison & Co. partnership: a professional engineer, not an entrepreneur.

Closing out the Newark factory, Edison purchased a hilltop site at an isolated spot called Menlo Park, about twenty-five miles from New York City. Menlo Park consisted, at the time, of some half dozen houses, so he was assured of privacy and rural seclusion. In the spring of 1876 construction began on the future laboratory, a barnlike wooden building of two stories. Edison's father, Sam Edison, came from Michigan to take charge of the operation.

Late in May the building was just about complete. It was 100 feet in length, 30 in width, painted a neat white, and surrounded by a picket fence to keep roving livestock away. From Newark came horse-drawn trucks laden with equipment—a steam engine, tools, boxes and jars of chemicals, bales of wire, batteries, gaslight apparatus, instruments of all sorts. Despite his misadventures with Jay Gould, Edison had achieved considerable solvency at Newark, and now he plowed much of his cash surplus into the purchase of the finest assortment of scientific material he could obtain.

From Newark, also, he brought the nucleus of his team: John Ott, Charles Batchelor, John Kruesi, Sigmund Bergmann, and about a dozen others. With their help, he said, he proposed to turn out "a minor invention every ten days and a big thing every six months or so."

The first "big thing" on the Menlo Park schedule was a project commissioned by Western Union which, in the spring of 1876, had not yet fallen into Jay Gould's clutches. After his fleecing by Gould, Edison had patched up his earlier quarrel with Western Union; for, little as he liked the telegraph company, it was the only market for his chief stock in trade now that he refused to do business with Gould.

Western Union wanted him to develop a speaking telegraph —that is, a telephone. Edison's experiments showed possibilities, but, as a deaf man, he found it hard to follow his own work. Meanwhile, a professor of phonetics named Alexander Graham Bell carried off the glory, filing for a patent on his telephone in February, 1876, while Edison was still at Newark.

Edison was disappointed, but he saw serious flaws in Bell's work, and set out to correct them. Bell had developed an adequate telephone receiver; his transmitter, though, was poor. Edison conceived a speaker altogether different from Bell's, which depended on a vibrating metal diaphragm. Edison's transmitting system used granules of carbon to control the flow of current through the diaphragm, with a striking improvement in the quality of the transmitted sound. He filed for a patent on his "speaking telegraph transmitter" on April 27, 1877, although much work remained to be done. In his notebook entry for July 17, 1877 he exclaimed: "Telephone perfected this morning at 5 A.M. Articulation perfect—got ¼ column newspaper every word." However, the first satisfactory demonstration of the Edison telephone did not take place until March, 1878. As the delighted directors of Western Union listened, Edison's transmitter carried messages clearly and loudly over a line one hundred and seven miles long between New York and Philadelphia.

By then the Bell backers had raised some money in Boston and were beginning to sell telephones to private customers. Bell Telephone's receiver was plainly superior to that of Edison's Western Union-backed American Speaking Telephone Company's instrument. For a transmitter, Bell merely borrowed the Edison speaker with minor changes. This was an infringement on the Edison patent, but not really much of a sin, since Edison's company was coolly infringing on the Bell receiver.

The mutual infringements led to an involved patent suit that began in September, 1878. Edison knew he had a better transmitter. He hoped he could somehow top Bell's receiver, but the logical outcome was some sort of compromise. Edison did actually produce a non-infringing substitute for the Bell receiver, but it had serious drawbacks, and after a year of litigation Western Union decided to settle out of court. Western Union sold its company, including Edison's speaker patent, to Bell in October of 1879. The price was a 20 per cent royalty on Bell's telephone rental income during the seventeen-year life of the patent, and ultimately totalled about $3,500,000. Edison's share came to a fee of $100,000. Now Edison's transmitter could legally be joined to Bell's receiver. Edison had made a significant and lasting contribution to telephony—though the credit for inventing the telephone has always gone to Alexander Graham Bell.

Edison's work with the telephone led him, more or less accidentally, into stumbling upon the phonograph. As he studied the problem of transmitting speech, he acquired insight into the much more difficult problem of reproducing speech. Working with a telephone receiver diaphragm in the summer of 1877, Edison noticed that its vibrations might be great enough to do mechanical work. What if a vibrating diaphragm, following recorded instructions, could be made to reproduce sound?

What he wanted was a machine that would take down spoken messages that could be transcribed later. Today's phonograph, pouring forth Bach, Beethoven, and the Beatles, did not occur to him then. Hoping to invent a useful business machine, Edison coated rolls of paper with paraffin and pulled them along a diaphragm that had a pin mounted in it. When one spoke into the diaphragm, a groove was cut on the paper; pulling the roll under a second diaphragm produced a faint, half-imaginary playback of the sounds.

Edison later told one of his biographers,

> Discovery is not invention, and I dislike to see the two words confounded. A discovery is more or less in the nature of an accident. A man walks along the road intending to catch the train. On the way his foot kicks against something

and . . . he sees a gold bracelet imbedded in the dust. He has discovered that—certainly not invented it. He did not set out to find a bracelet, yet the value is just as great.

The phonograph was both a discovery and an invention for Edison. Its true possibilities came upon him unawares, after he had put in long hours of painstaking inventive labor, the "98 per cent perspiration" that he liked to say went with the "2 per cent inspiration."

Late in 1877, although deep in the controversy with Bell over the telephone and enmeshed in Jay Gould's patent machinations with the telegraph, Edison found time to design a phonograph. He had come to understand the value of advance publicity, and so word was leaked to the influential *Scientific American* while work was still in the preliminary stages. The man who beat the drums for the phonograph was Edward H. Johnson, the engineer who had come to Edison to work on the automatic telegraph and who had remained with him. The Johnson-inspired article, published on November 17, 1877, spoke of a device that would record the human voice on paper, so that incoming telephone messages could be taken down and played back. But Edison was already past the idea of using coated paper, and had fixed on tinfoil as his recording medium.

On November 29, he drew a quick sketch of a machine to cut grooves with a needle into a tinfoil-covered cylinder as a crank was turned. Edison sent for John Kruesi and gave him the sketch. Edison's men were paid on a minimum-salary-plus-piecework-bonus basis, and Edison calculated that the job would be worth about eighteen dollars to Kruesi. "I am going to make a machine that talks," said Edison. "You complete that model and I will show you what it will do."

Kruesi, for all his great faith in Edison, was openly skeptical. Nonetheless he set to work with his usual skill. After thirty hours of virtually consecutive work, Kruesi returned with the model, a compact brass and iron device with a three-and-one-half-inch-long cylinder on a foot-long shaft. Edison wrapped a thin sheet of tinfoil around the cylinder, leaned toward the diaphragm tube, began to turn the handle, and bellowed into the tube the nursery jingle, "Mary had a little lamb." A little group of watching workmen smiled and exchanged amused glances as Edison returned the cylinder to the starting point, adjusted the playback diaphragm, and cranked the handle once again.

Faintly but distinctly from the diaphragm came the Mother Goose rhyme in Edison's high-pitched voice. "*Mein Gott im Himmel!*" cried Kruesi in awe. The other workmen gasped; they had seen Edison do many clever things, but never before had he worked a miracle. Edison himself admitted, "I was never so taken aback in my life."

All night long Edison and Kruesi took turns singing, whistling, shouting, and declaiming into the instrument. In ghostly but recognizable tones it reproduced their sounds. At daybreak, Edison wrapped the phonograph up and took it to New York to display it to F. C. Beach. That hard-bitten, skeptical editor of the *Scientific American* wrote:

> I had not been at my desk very long that morning when Mr. Edison was announced. He came in, and set his parcel, which he appeared to handle somewhat carefully, on my desk. As he was removing the cover, I asked him what it was.
>
> "Just a minute!" replied young Edison.
>
> Presently with a "here you are," he pushed the quaint-looking little instrument toward me. As there was a long shaft having a heavy wheel at one end and a small handle at the other, naturally I gave the handle a twist, and, to my astonishment, the unmistakable words, emitted from a kind of telephone mouthpiece, broke out, "Good morning! What do you think of the phonograph?"
>
> To say that I was astonished is a poor way of expressing my first impressions, and Edison appeared to enjoy his little joke on me immensely. Like a flash the news went among the staff that Edison had brought in a machine which could

talk, and soon there was an excited crowd around my desk.
. . . Edison was kept going for two or three hours, but at
last the crowd attained such proportions that I feared the
floor would give way under the abnormal weight, and I
requested the inventor to stop.

It is not easy for us to comprehend the impact that the phonograph made in the winter of 1877-78. Our imaginations have
been dulled by such a stream of wonders that we take everything for granted, from space journeys to video tape recorders to
color television. But to the dazed onlookers that December day
in 1877, Edison's little machine was overwhelming. Was anything more fleeting, less enduring, than the spoken word? Yet
here was a thing of brass and iron and tin that captured the
syllables as they fell from the lips, and sealed them forever to be
heard again and again!

Edison applied for a patent on the phonograph on December
15, 1877, about a week after his visit to the *Scientific American.*
The Patent Office examiners searched their files and reported
that this was an absolutely new invention, lacking even in the
usual assortment of misconceived predecessors. No attempt had
ever been made before to patent a device to record and produce
sound. The patent was granted in the unusually brief period of
fifty-seven days.

It was the phonograph that gave Edison his popular nickname, "the Wizard of Menlo Park." Newspapers and magazines
could find little else to discuss all winter. Edison was summoned
to Washington to display the machine at the home of Senator
James G. Blaine. All day long he cranked the handle while sena-
tors and cabinet ministers clustered around in disbelief. About
eleven that evening a White House messenger arrived to say
that President Hayes wished a demonstration. Edison hurried
down Pennsylvania Avenue with his invention under his arm to
entertain the President and several guests. Mrs. Hayes was
awakened, and until three thirty in the morning the thirty-one-

year-old "wizard" performed his magic for the chief executive of the nation.

There were many skeptics, of course, among those who had not seen the phonograph in action. There was dark talk of ventriloquism or some other kind of fraud. Among the doubters was Bishop John H. Vincent of the Methodist Episcopal Church, a leading clergyman of the day. Bishop Vincent journeyed to Menlo Park and carried out an acid test. Stepping to the tube, he shouted out a string of Biblical names that, Edison said, would "stop a clock." He called them forth with a nimble tongue: "Mahalaleel, Methuselah, Arphaxad, Hazarmaveth, Chedorlaomer," and many more. Back went the cylinder, round went the crank, and the jawbreakers were repeated. "I am satisfied," declared the Bishop. "There isn't a man in the United States who could recite those names with the same rapidity."

The *Scientific American,* in an assessment of Edison published at the end of 1878, declared,

> We are inclined to regard him as one of the wonders of the world. While Huxley, Tyndall, Spencer and other theorists talk and speculate, he produces accomplished facts, and with his marvelous inventions is pushing the whole world ahead in its march to the highest civilization.

From *Nature,* the leading British scientific journal, came a comment a few months later that must have pleased Edison even more:

> Mere ingenuity in contriving machines does not add to the sum of human knowledge, and if Mr. Edison were merely a clever inventor and nothing more, I should feel less interest in the man. It is, however, a noticeable feature of his inventions that they, in general, contain some new principles, some original observation in experimental science, which entitles him to the rank of a discoverer.

All this attention left Edison fundamentally unchanged. He had always had a high opinion of his own abilities, and now most of the world had come to share that opinion. That was all. His financial future was now secure, and he was certain of having the freedom and leisure he needed in order to make further conquests. He did not turn, as some other successful inventors of the day had done, to yachts, diamond stickpins, and race-horses. He lived well but not extravagantly, reinvesting most of his royalty profit in an expansion of the Menlo Park laboratory. He was still accumulating scientific books and instruments by carload lots, still spending more than half his waking hours at work, leaving his wife to cope with three small children without him. He was the prototype of the dedicated researcher, to whom little mattered but the work at hand. And in many ways he was still a country boy, though not a simple one; his attitude toward fame and fortune was wry and detached, as though he found it tremendously funny that so many people would make such a fuss over one man. Crowds of curiosity-seekers now made the pilgrimage to Menlo Park to catch a glimpse of the great inventor and his works, and Edison obligingly made himself available. Looking rumpled, slightly disreputable, and much younger than anyone expected, he answered questions in clear, homely language, accepted flamboyant compliments gracefully, and tolerated the gasps and gapes of a multitude of fools and bores. Behind his warmth and good humor lay an impenetrable core of reserve that was not entirely the result of his deafness. He was willing to be stared at and besieged by the public; yet his soul remained his private property. He was a most down-to-earth kind of wizard.

At the outset of 1878 he seemed convinced that in the phonograph he had hit the golden bonanza that would underwrite all his future experiments. He wrote an article for an influential magazine, the *North American Review,* in which he declared,

69

Among the many uses to which the phonograph will be applied are the following: 1) Letter-writing and all kinds of dictation without the aid of a stenographer; 2) Phonographic books which will speak to blind people without effort on their part; 3) The teaching of elocution; 4) The reproduction of music; 5) The Family Record (a registry of sayings, reminiscences, etc., by members of a family in their own voices), and of the last words of dying persons; 6) Music boxes and toys; 7) Clocks that should announce in articulate speech the time for going home, time for meals, etc.; 8) The preservation of languages by exact reproduction of the manner of pronouncing; 9) Educational purposes, such as preserving the explanations made by a teacher so that the pupil can refer to them at any moment; and spelling or other lessons placed upon the phonograph for convenience in committing to memory; 10) Connection with the telephone so as to make that instrument an auxiliary in the transmission of permanent and invaluable records, instead of being the recipient of momentary and fleeting communication.

It was a comprehensive list, and its comprehensiveness shows the penetrating power of Edison's mind. Just a few months earlier he had conceived of only a tenth of the use for his phonograph, but now a full panorama of purposes had unrolled itself in his mind. It would be many years, of course, before some of these uses for the phonograph materialized. Edison himself suggested, in the same article, "The phonograph will undoubtedly be largely devoted to music—either vocal or instrumental."

In January, 1878, a group of investors formed the Edison Speaking Phonograph Company, which purchased exclusive rights to manufacture phonographs primarily for use as music boxes. Among the stockholders was Gardiner Greene Hubbard, the father-in-law of Alexander Graham Bell. Edison received $10,000 down, and a guaranteed royalty of 20 per cent on each phonograph sold. The phonographs were to be manufactured by Sigmund Bergmann, who had opened his own electrical equip-

70

ment shop in downtown New York City. A company prospectus declared that the device was being offered to the public only as a novelty, since it was not yet fully adapted to "the practical uses of commerce."

Primitive as it was, the Edison phonograph touched off an instant craze. Some five hundred phonograph parlors sprang up, at which a fee was charged to listen to a phonograph crank out popular ditties and the jokes of music-hall comedians. At first the attendance was phenomenal; Edison's royalties for one week's attendance in Boston alone came to $1,800. But for most people, a single visit to the phonograph parlor was enough. The clever toy discharged its impact all at once. The tinfoil records played scarcely more than a minute, and wore out after a few playings. At best, the quality of sound reproduction was poor, and in the hands of inexperienced operators the results often were distressingly crude.

Edison knew that his phonograph had grave flaws and had been launched prematurely. During the spring of 1878 he pursued several paths toward its modification. Tinfoil was obviously inadequate, so he considered making his records on wax. He collected samples of virtually every known fat in the world, and put half a dozen men to work melting, blending, and mixing until he had a wide range of waxes to use. An attempt to make flat disk-shaped wax records ran into technical problems, and Edison returned to the original cylinder format. But the wax cylinders were fragile and needed careful handling. Edison found himself making little real progress. Nor did he get very far on other mechanical improvements in the diaphragm and pickup needle.

The original concept of the phonograph had leaped full-blown into Edison's mind; to make the machine commercially acceptable would require a series of slow, patience-trying steps that might take years. Edison in mid-1878 was in no mood to embark on such an endeavor. He had not had a real vacation since his wedding journey to Niagara Falls in 1871. For seven years he had lived under habitual strain, coping with dozens of stubborn technical problems while also fighting patent suits and foiling the schemes of the moneymen. He was tired, and to his own annoyance and surprise he was ill. Reluctantly he had to admit that he was not a machine for producing inventions, but a human being vulnerable to human ills. He needed a rest.

A friend, Professor George F. Barker of the University of Pennsylvania, suggested that he drop his work and join an expedition that was going to the Rocky Mountains to observe a total eclipse of the sun. Edison accepted. He abandoned work on the phonograph late in the spring of 1878.

The miraculous device was destined to gather dust on its shelf for a full decade. When Edison came back from the Rockies, it was with a new obsession—to invent a practical incandescent electric light. Soon he would refer slightingly to the phonograph as "a mere toy, which has no commercial value," as he plunged boldly into the greatest technological adventure of his life.

five

Let There
Be Light

WHEN Edison first became seriously interested in the prospects of the incandescent light, in the summer of 1878, a rival form of electric illumination was well entrenched and growing fast. This wonder of the age was the arc light, which seemed destined for great commercial success. Of course, the arc light had certain basic flaws that rendered it unfit for home use. For that reason Edison was contemptuous of its prospects, but to other observers the rapid spread of the arc light was so dazzling that it seemed to sweep incandescence into oblivion.

During the years when Grove and De Moleyns and Swan had been struggling with the incandescent light, another group of inventors had followed the path toward the arc light. They, too, were hampered at first by the need to rely on weak batteries for their power. The technical difficulties of designing a successful arc light were far less mountainous, though, than those confronting the researchers into incandescence.

The arc light's illumination was no gentle glow, but a furious and spectacular brilliance that surged with crackling intensity across the gap between two electrified carbon rods. Early problems included procuring carbon of proper purity and regulating the alignment of the rods—and, of course, obtaining enough power to keep the lamp running. The carbon was consumed as it produced light, and if the rods were not kept close together as they burned down, the light would die. By 1846, W. E. Staite— a pioneering worker with incandescent lights—had developed an ingenious and intricate means for keeping the rods together. He found that the heat radiated by the arc increased as the carbons were consumed and the length of the arc grew longer. In Staite's lamp, the heat thus generated caused a copper wire to expand, lifting a ratchet that permitted a weighted gear to raise the lower carbon. In the 1850's came modifications even more clever and more precise, but in the absence of a power source there was no use even for the cleverest arc light. Between 1860 and 1870 no arc light improvements were patented.

The advent of the Gramme ring-wound dynamo in 1870 brought on a hectic flurry of renewed activity. Gramme's own factory in Paris installed arc lights in 1873, arousing great public interest. There was immediate demand for other arc light installations; one of the first was in a German mill where four Gramme dynamos were used to operate four arc lights. Using one dynamo to power a single arc light was an enormously expensive way of doing things, but no one yet knew how to wire several lamps to one power source. In any case, the ferocious glare of a single arc light was capable of illuminating a large segment of the mill.

Other factories adopted arc lights later in 1875; the following year a railway company installed them on the platform of one station. By September of 1877, a single dynamo was supplying power to a 12-lamp installation at the railway station in Lyons. August of 1878 saw six arc lights illuminating the facade of the Gaiety Theatre in London, the work being done by French contractors. A contemporary observer described the effect as like that of "half a dozen harvest moons shining at once in the Strand."

74

While arc lights were thus conquering the cities of Europe, a new and vastly improved design made the conquest all the easier. This was the Jablochkoff candle, the work of Paul Jablochkoff, a Russian telegraph engineer living in Paris. Jablochkoff's "candle," invented in 1876, was an arc light consisting of two parallel carbon rods mounted vertically and separated by a porcelain plate. A strip of graphite connected the carbon rods at their tips. When the current was turned on, the graphite strip burned away and an arc formed in the gap. As the two pencil-thick rods were consumed, the arc maintained itself until they were gone. The Jablochkoff candle required no intricate mechanisms to keep the rods close together. Since they stood side by side instead of end to end, they would remain aligned so long as equal quantities of current were delivered to them. For this, alternating current was required, and the Gramme dynamos had to be modified to produce it.

The Jablochkoff candle represented a major stride forward in arc light technology, and it won immediate acceptance. In the spring of 1877 a large Paris department store, the Grands Magasins du Louvre, installed 80 of them, supplied with power by Gramme dynamos driven by a steam engine in the basement. The Avenue de l'Opéra was brightened by 46 lamps powered by three dynamos; the Place de l'Opéra had 22 lamps. Shortly the Jablochkoff candle spread to Great Britain. The first installation there, 6 lamps, went into service at an ironworks in Shoreditch on October 15, 1878, and a month later 16 Jablochkoff candles were lighting London's Billingsgate Fish Market.

The new light was not an unqualified success. For one thing, the carbon rods had to be replaced every day or so; for another, the glaring, hissing lamps were esthetically offensive. Among the dissenters was Robert Louis Stevenson, who wrote,

> A new sort of urban star now shines out nightly, horrible, unearthly, obnoxious to the human eye; a lamp for a nightmare! Such a light as this should shine forth only on murders

75

and public crime, or along the corridors of lunatic asylums, a horror to heighten horror. To look at it only once is to fall in love with gas. . . .

Despite such reactions, there were more than four thousand Jablochkoff candles in service by 1881. At Sheffield, England, thirty thousand spectators had witnessed a football game by electric light in 1878. The *Times* of London placed the new light in its printing office that year. British coal mines were electrified, as were railway stations in London and Glasgow, and the Reading Room of the British Museum.

The United States had seen its first public display of arc lights, a small one, at the Centennial Exposition of 1876. In the same year, twenty-seven-year-old Charles F. Brush of Cleveland persuaded the Cleveland Telegraph Supply Company to finance his attempt to build a dynamo more efficient than the standard Gramme dynamo of the day. Brush constructed a powerful dynamo which he patented in April of 1877, assigning manufacturing rights to his sponsor. Then he devised a new type of arc light that employed magnetic control to keep the carbons always at a given length and at the proper distance from one another. Brush's early dynamo was a one-light machine, but soon he had a larger model that could supply 16 lights at once. The lights were wired in series, which meant that if one lamp failed somewhere along the string, all the others would go out. Brush met this flaw by inventing a shunt coil—a short-circuiting device that would automatically carry the current around any disabled lamp to the others in the series, keeping the circuit unbroken. This was a significant advance over the various European systems of wiring, and now Brush was ready to seek commercial contracts for his arc lights.

His prospects were enhanced greatly early in 1878 when the Franklin Institute of Philadelphia decided to hold comparative scientific tests of available dynamos, before purchasing one for its own research. The Institute borrowed a Gramme dynamo, two of Brush's small dynamos, and two produced by another American engineer, William Wallace of Connecticut. The Gramme and Wallace machines had been demonstrated at the 1876 exposition; the Brush dynamos were unknown quantities. The testing committee consisted of two Philadelphia high school teachers, Elihu Thomson and Edwin J. Houston. Thomson, a precocious experimenter who had built his first friction generator and Leyden jar at the age of eleven, had been named an assistant professor of chemistry at Boys' Central High School when he was eighteen, in 1871. Five years later he succeeded to the full professorship. He had delivered an extraordinary series of lectures on electricity at the Franklin Institute when he was twenty-three, and had demonstrated then his own small direct-current generating system. Houston, six years his colleague's senior, had no such record of brilliance, but his knowledge of electrical theory was sound and comprehensive.

For several months Professors Thomson and Houston put the array of dynamos through their paces. They reported that the Gramme dynamo was the most efficient, with a rating of 38 per cent. The two Brush dynamos had efficiencies of 31 per cent and 27 per cent. But they yielded the most powerful current, and so produced the best light. At the recommendation of Thomson and Houston, the Institute purchased a Brush dynamo.

Among those who studied the results of the test with interest was John Wanamaker, Philadelphia's merchant prince. Wanamaker had been fascinated with electricity since the great exposition of 1876. He had recently converted the Pennsylvania Railroad's former freight depot at Thirteenth and Market Streets into a giant department store, daringly located far uptown in the expectation that Philadelphia would grow north to meet it. It seemed like a good idea to bolster his reputation for adventurousness by lighting his new store with electricity. He bought a Brush generating system and installed 28 Brush lamps in the store in December of 1878. The timing was shrewd. Phila-

delphians came far out of their way to see the miraculous lights
—and remained to do their Christmas shopping. A contemporary observer called them "miniature moons on carbon points,
held captive in glass globes."

Arc lighting created the same sensation in America as it had,
a few months before, in Europe. Brush's home town of Cleveland was the first city to adopt outdoor arc lighting, on April 29,
1879. Twelve lamps, mounted on 18-foot posts, received current
from a Brush dynamo in the shop of the Telegraph Supply
Company. It was the forerunner of many street lighting installations in which gigantic arc lamps, rising on masts more than a
hundred feet high, would rival the sun in brilliance and turn
night into day. The Cleveland *Plain Dealer* described the scene
the next day:

> Thousands of people gathered . . . and as the light shot
> around and through the Park a shout was raised. Presently
> the Grays Band struck up in the pavilion, and soon after-
> ward a section of artillery on the lake shore began firing a
> salute in honor of the occasion.
>
> The light varied some in intensity, when shining its
> brightest being so dazzling as to be painful to the eyes. In
> color it is of a purplish hue, not unlike moonlight, and by
> contrast making the gas lights in the store windows look a
> reddish yellow.

In a mere two months more the gospel of the Brush light had
reached California—a remarkable event at a time when the
difficulty of communication often made it seem as though the
western states were on some other planet. But California had
long been attentive to the possibilities of electricity. Father
Joseph Neri, a Jesuit of scientific inclinations, had kindled a
battery-powered arc light in San Francisco as early as 1871.
Three years later, having received a French dynamo as a gift,
the priest set up a searchlight atop the bell tower of St. Ignatius
College on Market Street; the glow, it was said with perhaps
too much enthusiasm, was visible for two hundred miles. And

78

on July 4, 1876, Father Neri illuminated the centennial parade with three startlingly bright arc lights. Another pioneering figure was Charles de Young of the San Francisco *Chronicle*, who came back from Paris in 1878 with a Gramme dynamo and two Jablochkoff candles. He installed the equipment in the *Chronicle's* new building at Bush and Kearny Streets, running the generator on the same engine that operated the presses.

San Francisco's California Electric Light Company, incorporated on June 30, 1879, holds a special place in the history of the electric light. It was the first power company in the world to have a central generating station for the distribution of electricity to private customers. Every existing electrical installation had been either municipal or for the exclusive use of the store, hotel, theater, or railroad that constructed it.

The Brush system got its foothold in California when the San Francisco Telegraph Supply Company obtained the Pacific Coast rights to market Brush equipment from the Brush Electric Company, as the Cleveland Telegraph Supply Company now styled itself. The California company installed several isolated lighting plants late in 1878, including one at a Yuba County gold mine, and attracted enough capital to establish the first electric utility company seven months later. In the summer of 1879 it set up a modest power plant in a frame building at Fourth and Market Streets. As George H. Roe, the company's president, explained a few years later, no one knew if the enterprise had a chance to be profitable, and so the capital risk was held to a minimum.

> Naturally, the cheapest building was constructed, simply 4x4 uprights, a wooden floor laid on the ground, the sides of the building covered with sheet iron. The boiler, engine, dynamos, oil house, coal pile, and everything was huddled together in this one enclosure. . . . We realized that the expenditure we were making was merely experimental and would be of no value if the business amounted to nothing.

79

The initial equipment included two Brush dynamos, one of 16-light capacity, the other a 5-light machine.

Service began in September, 1879. The company offered to sell light to customers from sundown to midnight at a cost of $10 per lamp per week. There was no service on Sundays or holidays. Nor was electricity offered for home use; as the company prospectus pointed out, "in dwellings it is not as cheap as gas or oil and is not yet adapted to such uses."

A clothing store and a jewelry shop were among the first customers. Soon the San Francisco Post Office was signed up, after the company offered

> 6 electric lights of 2000 candlepower each sufficient to light the office and entrance which will make a very fine light not trying to the eye as gas light for the sum of $450 per month. . . . Remember that in the foregoing estimate we intend to furnish double lamps that will burn 16 hours without attention. The single lamps burn 8 hours and there is no other electric lamp giving a good light, except ours (The Brush Lamp) that will burn longer than one hour and a half.

In time, the city itself purchased service, setting up a street lighting system of twenty-one 50-foot masts, each bearing four 4,000-candlepower lamps. Business was so good that within three months the new company had to add a pair of 16-light dynamos, and it bought two more a few months later.

And so the arc light industry grew. On July 4, 1879, Niagara Falls was illuminated by a 16-light Brush dynamo and a set of arc lamps. The dynamo was powered by a waterwheel, making it perhaps the first hydroelectric generator. Arc lights were installed in Boston and Cincinnati, and there was talk of using them to light the streets of New York. The small community of Wabash, Indiana won a brief moment of national attention in March of 1880 when it became the first town wholly lighted by electricity, a Brush installation of four 3000-candlepower lamps, mounted on crossarms atop the courthouse dome, 200 feet high.

More than ten thousand people were on hand the moonless night of March 31 to see the circuit put into operation. Among them were reporters from many newspapers. The Fort Wayne *Daily Sentinel* told how,

> Promptly as the courthouse clock struck eight, the thousands of eyes that were turned toward the inky darkness over the courthouse saw a shower of sparks emitted from a point above them, small, steady spots of light, growing more brilliant until within a few seconds after the first sparks were seen, it was absolutely dazzling. A loud shout went up from the crowd, the band began to play. . . .

A man from the Chicago *Tribune* went "up into the dome, right under the light," and there "beheld a scene of magnificent splendor. For a mile around, the houses and yards were distinctly visible, while the far-away river flowed like a band of molten silver."

It seemed to many, by the spring of 1880, that the arc light was destined for permanent dominance. There was at least one conspicuous skeptic, though, and he was a figure of some consequence in this field.

Edison had had some preliminary thoughts about electricity as early as 1875. He cast a wide net, and tried to keep up in some fashion with nearly every scientific development. So when news came to him of the arc lights being commercially installed in France and Germany, Edison took time out from his telegraph work to investigate them. He made an electric arc light of exposed carbon points and connected it to a 31-cell battery. It glowed for a minute or two, hissing and sizzling all the while. Then it went out. With that his experiment ended.

In the summer of 1876 some momentary byway of Edison's work got him toying with carbonized paper. He passed a current through a strip of carbonized paper and watched it become briefly incandescent. The idea occurred that such paper might be useful in "electric lighting and batteries," and he noted it in

81

his journal. Then the urgency of the telephone project called him away, and kept him away for a year, leaving a clear field to such men as Brush and Wallace.

It seems surprising, at first thought, that Edison was so late in coming to electricity. A gadgeteer from boyhood, a rapt admirer and student of the work of Faraday, why had he left the field to Brush and Wallace and Farmer and the others? Why had he not given the world light long ago?

For one thing, Edison was primarily a telegraph man. He had begun as an operator, had moved on to make some mechanical improvements in the apparatus he used, and then by a natural progression had been led from the telegraph to the telephone to the phonograph. None of these devices required any large-scale supply of electric power. They kept him busy enough so that he had no occasion to turn toward what appeared to be an unrelated challenge, the production and distribution of electricity.

For another, Edison had no very profound grasp of the theory of electricity. His gift was for the three-dimensional visualization of equipment. Something like a phonograph would spring into his mind, and he was able to sketch it clearly enough for a John Kruesi to build a working model in a few days. The abstract, the intangible, the theoretical were not really his specialties. He could follow Faraday, because Faraday had put a copper disk and a magnet together and had produced a current. But the brilliant equations of Clerk Maxwell that showed how electricity and magnetism were related were beyond Edison's grasp. If Edison knew anything of Clerk Maxwell's work, he left no clue of it, nor was it necessary for Clerk Maxwell to have lived at all for Edison to have carried out his own work. Edison was largely innocent of theory, although once he became seriously involved with electricity he learned what he had to learn, and learned it magnificently. Since he had no desire to find out about electricity in the abstract, he gave the subject little priority until some immediate and practical end presented itself.

Lastly, Edison did not really come "late" to electricity. He was only thirty-one when he began his search for the incandescent light, and he had been an extremely busy man in the decade just concluded. Of his other projects, one had been a significant improvement in Bell's telephone—an impressive accomplishment that won him widespread public attention. His other enterprise was the machine to record and play back sound, the phonograph. To the world of 1877, the phonograph seemed with some justification to be actual black magic. When news came that this extraordinary man was putting aside his phonograph to work on electric lights, a ripple of anticipation was instantly produced.

Edison was already legendary at thirty. Marshall Fox, writing of him in the pages of *Scribner's* in 1879, described the public's attitude toward Edison in these words:

The hero of their labors assumed all sorts of forms. Now he was a scientific hermit shut up in a cavern in a small New Jersey village, holding little or no intercourse with the outside world, working like an alchemist of old in the dead of night, with musty books and curious chemicals, and having for his immediate companions persons as weird and mysterious as himself. Again he was a rollicking, careless person, highly gifted in matters scientific, but deplorably ignorant of everything else, a sort of scientific Blind Tom. Especially was he credited with the most revolutionary ideas concerning Nature. One Western journal represented him as predicting a complete overthrow of nearly all the established laws of Nature: water was no longer to seek its level; the earth was speedily to assume new and startling functions in the universe; everything that had been learned concerning the character of the atmosphere was based on error; the sun itself was to be drawn up in ways that are dark, and to be made subsidiary to innumerable tricks that are vain; in short, all Nature was to be upset.

Somewhat less fanciful was this sketch of Edison from an 1878 issue of *Popular Science Monthly:*

Of the number of persons in the laboratory, remark one you may have least thought of selecting from the informality of his appearance. It is a figure of perhaps five feet nine inches in height, bending above some detail of work. There is a general appearance of youth about it, but the face, knit into anxious wrinkles, seems old. The dark hair, beginning to be touched with gray, falls over the forehead in a mop. The hands are stained with acid, and the clothing is of an ordinary ready-made order. It is Edison. He has the air of a mechanic, or, more definitely, with his peculiar pallor, of a night printer. His features are large; the brow well shaped, without unusual developments; the eyes light gray, the nose irregular, and the mouth displaying teeth which are also not altogether regular. When he comes up his attention comes back slowly as though it had been a long way off. But it comes back fully and gradually and the expression of the face, now that it can be seen, is frank and prepossessing. A cheerful smile chases away the grave and somewhat weary look that belong to it in moments of rest. He seems no longer old. He has almost the air of a big, careless school-boy released from his desk.

Thus did Edison's contemporaries view him in the late 1870's. He was only on the threshold of real greatness then. Seeing him in the perspective of his complete career, we find it all the more difficult to resist calling him a wizard.

The entry of Thomas Edison into the race to perfect the electric light put a new outlook on things. A mere eight years had passed since the invention of the Gramme dynamo had fostered the current interest in electricity. The widespread commercial use of the arc light had begun only in 1877. A few men had started work a year or two in advance of Edison on the arc light's successor, but, though he missed out on a place in the very first rank of electrical pioneers, within a year he was following hot on their heels.

His telephone speaker was perfected by the early autumn of 1877, and, with that great task completed, Edison took another look at electric lighting. He built some open arc lights having strips of carbonized paper as burners, and made tentative efforts toward designing an incandescent light. He mounted carbon strips under a glass bell jar and pumped out the air, using a hand-operated vacuum pump. The vacuum was a poor one and the carbons lasted just a few minutes. Edison tried mounting such metals as boron, chromium, and ruthenium in his bulb; he investigated powdered silicon in glass tubes, both with and without a mixture of lime; he sampled a variety of other materials that might produce a long-lived incandescent effect. As winter approached, he had nothing to show for his labors. Meanwhile the first working phonograph had been produced, and in the six-month sensation that followed Edison scarcely thought at all about electric lights.

Then came his illness and his disenchantment with the phonograph. July of 1878 saw him in Wyoming as the guest of his physicist friend, Professor Barker. Of course, Edison had found a way to contaminate his vacation with work: he brought along a newly invented instrument he called the "tasimeter," which was sensitive to minute changes in temperature. Edison believed his tasimeter could measure temperature deviations as slight as a millionth of a degree Fahrenheit, and he intended to test it by registering the changes in the sun's heat during the eclipse.

There were dozens of astronomers, physicists, and other authentic scientists in the party, and Edison's presence among them created some unvoiced tensions. Though the general public regarded Edison as a great scientist, he was nothing of the kind, simply an inspired inventor, with no pretensions to the contrary. Some of the more austere scientific men resented Edison's national prestige, inwardly regarding him as an impostor, though it was scarcely his fault that laymen insisted on confusing pure science with engineering. The scientists tended to be a little condescending toward him. For his part, Edison saw most of the scientists as dreamy dilettantes who lived in ivory towers, and he was mildly contemptuous of their impracticality.

None of these hidden feelings ever rose to the surface. Edison's frankness and charm quickly won him many new friends among the scientists. And Edison watched in undisguised awe on the day of the eclipse as the scientists began to make their calculations. He said afterward:

> They first set up their instruments to determine their exact position on the earth and its relation to the sun. I was amazed at the immense amount of mathematics, and preserved one of their sheets; it looked like the timetable of a Chinese railroad. They found they were not in error more than one hundred feet. It was a revelation to me on the precision of the astronomers and the physicists.

Edison assembled his own apparatus in a nearby hen house. As the sky darkened, he noticed, the hens went to their roosts. Just after the moment of totality a violent storm broke out, and Edison found himself in a disintegrating shelter, trying desperately to keep his telescope trained on the sun and check his other instruments while feathers flew and hens squawked wildly. Somehow he completed the experiment, only to find that the heat from the sun's corona was ten times greater than the index capacity of the tasimeter. So he learned nothing from the eclipse about the instrument's sensitivity.

He did get a fine rest, though. There were lively moments, as when a two-gun swaggerer called "Texas Jack" insisted on entertaining the famed inventor with a display of marksmanship. Drawing his Colt, Texas Jack aimed from Edison's hotelroom window at a weather vane down the street and impressively shot it from its stand. A little alarmed, Edison got rid of the man by pleading the need for sleep. After the eclipse, Edison joined a hunting party and was permitted to ride the cow-catcher of the locomotive. At one point the train struck an animal about the size of a bear, which came hurtling up toward Edison. He ducked just in time to avoid being knocked flying.

While Edison was enjoying these exploits, a shrewd lawyer named Grosvenor P. Lowrey was quietly hatching a plot to get him interested once more in electric lighting. Lowrey, a patent lawyer and general counsel for Western Union, was perhaps Edison's most enthusiastic and well-informed admirer. Since 1876 he had taken to spending as much of his time at Menlo Park as in the offices of Western Union, and knew nearly as much about the inventor's activities as Edison did himself. Sixteen years older than Edison, Lowrey was a man well versed in the ways of Wall Street, and had begun to function as Edi-son's ambassador to the world of high finance.

Lowrey had attended the Paris Exposition of 1878. Among the conspicuous sights at that fair was a glittering array of Jablochkoff candles. This efficient new type of arc light seemed to be sweeping Paris; and, by the bright glare of the Jabloch-koff candles on the Avenue de l'Opéra, Lowrey saw an exciting opportunity for Edison. To go beyond the arc light—to get electric illumination into the home, into stores and offices—could it be done? Was there a way of supplanting the huge, brilliant arc lights with some smaller, gentler system of lighting by electricity? Lowrey was no scientist, and had no understand-ing of the technical problems involved, but he knew Edison's capabilities. If anyone could do it, it was Edison. So Lowrey collected a thick file of information on the Jablochkoff candle and forwarded it to Menlo Park, hoping that it would stir Edison's imagination when he returned from the wild west.

Others had had the same idea. In the spring of 1878 Colonel George E. Gouraud, Edison's representative in England, had written to urge the inventor to take up the electric light.

87

Gouraud had cited recent European successes in arc lighting. But Edison, gripped by fatigue, had turned the idea down at that time, because, he said, "so many others were working in that field." Two months later, on the vacation trip, Professor Barker had independently renewed the theme. Barker, a leading physicist of his day, was keenly interested in the electric light and had already made some preliminary analysis of the technical challenge it presented. Barker's words gave Edison the spur he needed. When he returned to Menlo Park and found Lowrey's data on Jablochkoff's light awaiting him, his resolve became firm.

He set down his goal concisely in his current notebook, volume 184:

> Object, Edison to effect exact imitation of all done by gas, so as to replace lighting by gas, by lighting by electricity.

six

Making
the Dream
Real

WHEN Edison had become interested in the commercial possibilities of the electric light in the summer of 1878, his first step,
as it had always been, was to see what the competition was
up to.

> When I want to discover something, I begin by reading
> up everything that has been done along that line in the
> past—that's what all these books in the library are for. I
> see what has been accomplished at great labor and expense
> in the past. I gather the data of many thousands of experi
> ments as a starting point, and then I make thousands more.

But he did not feel like going to Cleveland to examine the
Brush factory; there was an arc light manufacturer closer at
hand, in Ansonia, Connecticut. Moses Farmer and William
Wallace were turning out dynamos and arc lights there that
had won some limited acceptance in New England. Farmer, a
veteran of electrical research, had lit his own home with arc
lights in 1859, and had built an outstanding dynamo seven years
later. Wallace's dynamo had been exhibited at the 1876 Centennial Exposition, and just then—in September, 1878—was

undergoing tests by Thomson and Houston at the Franklin Institute.

Edison had no difficulty gaining access to the Wallace-Farmer factory. In a period of general buccaneering, he was respected as much for his honesty as for his technical brilliance, and there was no fear that he would stoop to stealing a usable idea. A visit from Edison was an honor. Wallace received him warmly and displayed his 8-horsepower dynamo, putting it to work lighting eight arc lights of 500 candlepower each.

Marshall Fox, a reporter for the New York *Herald* who often covered Edison's doings, was on hand. He wrote,

> Edison was enraptured. . . . He fairly gloated. . . . He ran from the instruments to the lights and then again from the lights back to the electric instruments. He sprawled over a table and made all sorts of calculations. He calculated the power of the instruments and the lights, the probable loss of power in transmission, the amount of coal the instrument would use in a day, a week, a month, a year. . . .

By the brilliant light the inventors solemnly toasted each other, and Edison signed his name on his goblet with a diamond stylus: "Thomas A. Edison, Sept. 8, 1878, made under the electric light." There was an amiable round of handshaking as Edison prepared to take his leave. Then Edison turned to Wallace and casually said, "I believe I can beat you making electric light. I do not think you are·working in the right direction."

Edison set down his views on what the right direction was shortly after he reached Menlo Park:

> I saw for the first time everything in practical operation. *I saw the thing had not gone so far but that I had a chance.* I saw that what had been done had never been made practically useful. The intense light had not been subdivided so that it could be brought into private houses. In all electric lights theretofore obtained the intensity of the light was

very great, and the quantity (of units)* very low. I came
home and made experiments two nights in succession. I
discovered the necessary secret, so simple that a bootblack
might understand it. It suddenly came to me, like the secret
of the speaking phonograph. It was real and no phantom.
. . . The subdivision of light is all right.

With remarkable foresight he sketched the future not only
of the electrical industry he proposed to create, but of the gas
industry he expected to displace:

> Gas will be manufactured less for lighting as the result
> of electrical competition and more for heating, etc., thus
> enlarging its market and increasing its income.
> It doesn't matter if electricity is used for light or power.
> . . . Small motors can be used night or day and small steam
> engines are inconvenient. . . . Generally, poorest district for
> light, best for power, thus evening up whole city—note the
> effect of this on investment.

The gas industry, a sleepy and complacent utility monopoly,
had scarcely thought about using gas for anything other than
lighting. The advantages of gas cooking had been demonstrated
as far back as 1830, while in the 1870's inventors had shown how
gas could be used for heating homes and for generating the
steam for steam-engine power. Gas stoves were first exhibited
in the United States in 1851, and were offered for sale from
1859 on. Yet in 1878 there were not a dozen gas stoves in use
in all of New York City, and perhaps a hundred in the nation.
Edison, even as he prepared to destroy the gas industry as a
force in illuminating, saw the possibilities that gas still held.
His prediction was remarkably accurate, for the gas industry
did not disappear once Edison's electric companies began to
compete with it. In 1884, when the giant Consolidated Gas
Company of New York was formed, 95 per cent of its income
came from lighting. Today the same company, now known as

* Edison means units of electrical resistance, now known as *ohms*.

Consolidated Edison Company of New York, sells both gas and electricity. Its gas revenue in 1965 was $104,291,000, almost all from cooking and heating.

Edison's other prediction—that electricity would be sold both for light and for power—revealed shrewd insight into the economics of the coming industry. He saw that a huge capital expenditure would be needed to provide the generating equipment; the only way a profit could be shown on that expenditure was by running the dynamos day and night, producing power for machinery during the day and lighting homes and streets after dark.

Here at the outset, then, Edison envisioned much more than the mere invention of a workable incandescent light. He was inventing a total industry. Having picked the incandescent light as the ideal way of lighting homes, he coolly proposed to create an entire system of generating, transmitting, and distributing electricity that would push aside its flawed competitors, arc lighting and gas lighting.

He had no doubt that he could offer a superior product. Arc lights were not even really competitive with what he had in mind, since they were too brilliant for practicable indoor use. As for gas lighting, it was dangerous, odorous, feeble, and costly. An advertisement for a nineteenth-century gas appliance unintentionally provides us with a vivid catalog of the defects of gas lighting:

SHERMAN AUTOMATIC GAS GOVERNORS
Gas Bills Reduced 15% to 40%.
Greater brilliance, steadier flame, no broken globes.
Security against fire.
No blowing nor smoking burners.
Insurance risks greatly reduced.
Marvelous sanitary effects.

No poisonous vapors from unconsumed gases. No vitiated atmosphere. No smoked-up walls, paintings or draperies.

Practical economy.

Save their cost every three months. Equal to 400% per annum. Paying investment.

You pay their cost to the gas company every three months, four times a year, and for indifferent light. Why?

Are they reliable and durable?

Constructed entirely of brass; no rubber nor leather diaphragms to be eaten up by gas and acids. No mercury to poison the atmosphere.

Are they appreciated?

Ask our thousands of patrons.

The National Gas Saving Company, 21 East 14th Street.

Any form of home lighting that needed so many safeguards to be minimally acceptable was at the mercy of Thomas Alva Edison.

Since he was taking aim primarily at the gas industry, Edison collected and studied everything he could find about gas: journals of the gas-engineering societies, reports of the gas companies, technical volumes. He compiled charts and tables on the economics of gas distribution. He hired an expert gas engineer to guide his investigations, but very soon the man observed that Edison knew as much about the gas business as anyone alive. Edison's notebooks began to incorporate dozens of notations on the drawbacks of gas: "So unpleasant is the effect of the products of gas that in the new Madison Square theatre every gas jet is ventilated by special tubes to carry away the products of combustion. . . ." To replace gas, he saw, he needed "a general system of distribution—the only possible means of economical illumination." And he told himself, "Edison's great effort—not to make a large light or a blinding light, but a small light having the mildness of gas." He concluded, "Having obtained all the data and investigated gas-jet distribution in New York by actual observations, I made up my mind that the problem of the subdivision of the electric current could be solved and made commercial."

The subdivision of the current: that was the mighty obstacle. Devising a workable incandescent bulb seemed like no problem at all to Edison; he merely had to find the right material to use and the right way to seal it in a vacuum. But "subdividing," as everyone agreed, was harder to accomplish.

The experts even disagreed on their definitions of subdivision. They talked of subdivision of the current, of the voltage, of the light itself, and thereby created much confusion. Edison saw the problem in greater detail than anyone.

He had to subdivide the light. That meant abandoning the arc light, with its 4000-candlepower glare, and offering a small light for the home, on the order of 16 candlepower, as was the household gas jet. Such a light would have to be under the customer's control and within his reach.

Existing arc lights worked on dangerously high amperages, or currents. The Brush arc lights that began to appear in city streets were beyond the reach of pedestrians, but there were horrifying cases of company linemen being electrocuted in the full view of frightened citizens. Edison knew that it was unthinkable to bring such potent currents into the home. To him, the secret of subdividing the light lay in subdividing the current.

Others knew the risks of using strong currents for home lighting. Some held that subdividing the current was physically impossible, a violation of the laws of conservation of energy. Some said it was possible but impractical, since, as they calculated, if one electric light of a thousand candlepower were divided into ten smaller lights and connected by ten equal branches, each would carry not a tenth, but one hundredth of the original light. Sir William H. Preece, Britain's ranking expert on electricity, put it in brisk technical language when addressing the Royal Institution in London on February 15, 1879:

> It is, however, easily shown . . . that in a circuit where the electromotive force [voltage] is constant, and we insert additional lamps, then when these lamps are joined in one circuit, i.e., in series, the light varies inversely as the square of the number of the lamps in circuit, and that joined up in multiple arc, the light diminishes as the cube of the number inserted. Hence a subdivision of the electric light is an absolute *ignis fatuus*.

Sir William's words carried conviction. Arc lights on the streets were generally wired in series, so that if one went out, an entire group would go out. But home electric lights had to be independent of one another, so that each customer could turn his lights off and on without affecting those of his neighbors. To do that, it was necessary to wire them in parallel, what Sir William called "multiple arc." Lights wired in parallel are strung between the lines instead of in the lines themselves. Each has its own small supply of electricity drawn from the main line. In brief, the all-important parallel wiring could be achieved only through subdivision—and subdivision, said the experts, was impossible.

Edison was not the only inventor to challenge that assertion. Swan in England, Moses Farmer and William Wallace in the United States, and a dozen others all sought to find some way around the puzzle of subdivision. Most of them saw that, Sir William Preece to the contrary, there was no real theoretical barrier to subdivision. The barrier was technical. They all designed lamps that required high currents—ten amperes or more. To make such lamps safe for home use and to make them feasible for parallel circuitry, they had to subdivide the voltage. Current would leave the dynamo at a high voltage, which somehow had to be stepped down radically before it got to the customer's house. Since power was the product of current and voltage, subdividing the voltage would achieve the same thing as subdividing the current.

Only one thing was wrong: neither Swan nor Farmer nor anyone else could find a way of subdividing the voltage.

Edison, in his early calculations, followed the conventional lines of thinking. He planned to design an incandescent light that would use about 10 amperes of current at a force of 10 volts. Like all other incandescent lamps then in the experimental stage, it would have a low electrical resistance of only one ohm.

The law of electrical resistance had been formulated in 1827 by the German physicist Georg Simon Ohm. Ohm had discovered that the intensity of the electric current flowing in a conductor is equal to the electromotive force divided by the resistance. (In modern electrical terms, the amperes in a circuit equal the voltage across it divided by the circuit's resistance in ohms.) Though this knowledge had been available for half a century, few of the would-be inventors of incandescent lights had availed themselves of it. They had viewed their problem as one of designing the lamp, not as one of distributing the current. To them, the stumbling block was the conductor, which kept burning out when in use. To keep the conductor from overheating, they made it thick and strong.

A thick conductor, though, has low electrical resistance—just as a wide valley offers low resistance to the flow of water. Water flows gently through such a valley, causing little turbulence or erosion. And electricity flows "gently" through a low-resistance conductor, producing little heat. The only way to make a low-resistance conductor incandescent is with a great deal of current.

Edison was aghast at how much current would actually be required to light up his low-resistance lamps. To push that much current any sizable distance through city streets called for high voltages, and there would be an unavoidable voltage drop every few blocks simply as a function of distance. Some quick work with a pencil showed him that he would need a colossal amount of copper wire to conduct the current within even a small district. Alternately, he could build a generating plant on every streetcorner. Either way, the capital expenses would be so mountainous that the project was an impossibility before it began.

Ohm's law of resistance, though, gave Edison his solution. It seems surprisingly obvious now, but it came with the force of revelation in 1878. Design a high-resistance lamp! Such a lamp would consume less current. Voltage would have to be raised, but that did not matter; what produced the expense was the current, not the voltage. Late in 1878 Edison recalculated his estimates on the basis of a light of 100 ohms resistance, using only one ampere of current at 100 volts, over the same distance of line and assuming the same drop of voltage with distance. He was pleasantly astonished to learn that just *one one-hundredth* as much copper would be needed in his distributing system. The high-resistance lamp was the key to an economically feasible electrical industry. That revelation seems to have occurred to Edison during his visit to the arc light factory of Moses Farmer and William Wallace on September 8, 1878.

He claimed later that the entire vision of the electrical industry flared up in his mind all at once, the way the entire plan of a symphony revealed itself to Mozart in an instant. In the course of later patent litigation over his electrical inventions, he issued this summary of the outlook he had faced in the autumn of 1878:

> A complete system of distribution for electricity had to be evolved, and as I had to compete with the gas system this must be commercially efficient and economical, and the network of conductors must be capable of being fed from many different points. A commercially sound network of distribution had to permit of being placed under or above

ground, and must be accessible at all points and be capable of being tapped anywhere.

I had to devise a system of metering electricity in the same way as gas was metered, so that I could measure the amount of electricity used by each consumer. These meters must be accurate so that we could charge correctly for the current used, and also they must be cheap to make and easy to read and keep in working order.

Means and ways had also to be devised for maintaining an even voltage everywhere on the system. The lamps nearest the dynamo had to receive the same current as the lamps farthest away. The burning out or breaking of lamps must not affect those remaining in the circuit, and means had to be provided to prevent violent fluctuations of current.

One of the largest problems of all was that I had to build dynamos more efficient and larger than any then made. Many electrical people stated that the *internal* resistance of the armature should be equal to the external resistance; but I made up my mind that I wanted to sell all the electricity I made and not waste half in the machine, so I made my internal resistance small and got out 90 per cent of saleable energy.

Over and above these things, many other devices had to be invented and perfected, such as devices to prevent excessive currents, proper switching gear, lamp holders, chandeliers, and all manner of details that were necessary to make a complete system of electric lighting that could compete successfully with the gas system. Such was the work to be done in the early part of 1878. The task was enormous but we put our shoulders to the wheel, and in a year and a half we had a system of electric lighting that was a success. During this period, I had upwards of one hundred energetic men working hard on all details.

One question concerning this early system has often been asked, namely: "Why did I fix 110 volts as a standard pressure for the carbon filament lamp?" The answer to this is that I based my judgment on the best I thought we could do in the matter of reducing the cost of copper and the difficulties we had in making filaments stable at high voltages. I thought that 110 volts would be sufficient to insure the commercial introduction of the system, and 110 volts is still the standard.

Perhaps Edison was being somewhat too generous with himself in all this. Contemplating his project late in 1878, he certainly saw the essential features: the high-resistance lamp, the central power stations, the constant voltage, the parallel wiring. But much of the implementation of these features emerged slowly over a period of four years, after lengthy processes of trial and error. The "Edison system," his greatest invention, took shape in gradual stages.

Without a lamp, he had nothing. So, while work progressed more or less simultaneously on all the various fronts of the problem, Edison's first thrust was toward designing an incandescent lamp. He needed a conductive substance, or "burner." The desired burner had to be able to endure fierce heat without fusing or melting or burning up, and—Edison's special requirement— it had to have a high electrical resistance.

Curiously, Edison's first lamps of September, 1878 were low-resistance lamps, even though they were conceived after the visit to Wallace in which he had grasped the way to subdivide the light. Perhaps he had not yet worked out a means of constructing a high-resistance lamp, or perhaps he simply wanted to traverse the state of the art. Most probably, the idea of a high-resistance lamp had not established itself as firmly in his mind at that time as he later said it had.

His first choice for the burner material was carbon, the favorite of all lamp-builders up to that time. Carbon was a good conductor and had a high melting point of 3500° C. In his preliminary tests Edison went back to his work of 1876, making strips of carbonized paper a sixteenth of an inch in width incandescent in open air, simply to see how much current was needed. Then he put his carbon strips into partially evacuated glass jars, and was able to keep them incandescent about eight minutes before they went out. That was hardly satisfactory; and in any event carbon was unfavorably associated in Edison's mind with the inefficient lamps of his predecessors and competitors.

He tested a variety of metals next—platinum, titanium, rhodium, and others. Among the ones he tried was tungsten, which today is the metal used in incandescent bulbs; but in 1878 there was no way to work this very hard but otherwise suitable metal into the form of wire, and Edison put it aside. Of all that he tried in the busy sessions between September 11 and September 26, 1878, platinum seemed the most likely. He inserted a spiral of platinum wire into a partial vacuum and quickly brought it to incandescence. But platinum's melting point was not far above its point of incandescence, as such pioneers as Grove, Staite, and De Moleyns had learned thirty years earlier. All too soon the heat of incandescence reached the fatal level, the wire melted, and the light went out.

Edison responded to this drawback with characteristic ingenuity. He built a lamp whose burner consisted of a vertical coil of platinum attached to a short platinum rod. When the current heated the platinum, the rod expanded; if the temperature became too high, the expansion of the rod would automatically short-circuit the burner and allow it to cool. This took place in an instant, so that the lamp merely blinked. Privately Edison doubted that such a lamp could ever win wide use, but after his custom of filing for a patent on anything that seemed remotely valuable, he sent in his patent application on October 5, 1878.

Dissatisfied with the first model, he designed a platinum lamp with a different type of regulator, then one with a platinum-iridium alloy for its burner, and then one whose burner was an inverted U-shaped tube of powdered iridium mixed with zirconium oxide. When cold, zirconium oxide does not conduct electricity, so the iridium alone yielded light until the zirconium oxide was hot enough to be conductive. Again, high marks for cleverness, but nothing of commercial value. After it came a lamp with a carbon rod pressed against a platinum-iridium rod, and several other variations.

This period of tinkering in September and October was useful for Edison. He was learning things about the resistance of various incandescing materials, and he was developing techniques for achieving a higher vacuum in his lamps. Also, now that he was actually enmeshed in the laboratory work, he was coming to see how absolutely essential it was to use a high-resistance lamp and parallel wiring. Anything else would require vast sums of money to establish the distribution system.

In making his calculations, Edison had the services of a professional mathematician, Francis R. Upton. Edison had a practical man's studied contempt for mathematics, preferring his own rule-of-thumb techniques. At the advice of Grosvenor Lowrey he reluctantly hired Upton in 1878. Upton had studied at Princeton and had spent a year in Germany working for the great physicist, Hermann von Helmholtz. Edison, admitting that Upton might have some uses, took him on, he said, because it was just as well "to have one mathematical fellow around, in case we have to calculate something out."

Edison took a malicious pleasure in putting the youthful Upton in his place. Soon after Upton arrived, Edison handed him a pear-shaped glass bulb and asked to know its cubic contents in centimeters. Upton took paper and pencil and began putting down equations. After about an hour, Edison asked him for the answer. "I'm about halfway through," said Upton. "I'll need more time."

"Why," Edison replied, "I would simply take that bulb, fill it with a liquid, and measure its volume directly." He meant that he would pour the liquid into a measuring flask and read the volume off the graduated scale. Upton was taken aback; the idea had not occurred to him at all. But once Edison was

101

involved with resistances and voltages, no measuring flasks were available, only the integral and differential equations that Upton could handle so well. Edison soon had him busy working out the mathematical basis for an unprecedented electrical system using high-resistance lamps in a parallel circuit. The assignment came as a surprise to Upton, who, like everyone else but Edison, had failed to see this obvious application of Ohm's law. He was amazed when Edison pointed out to him that raising the resistance of the proposed lamp and the voltage of the dynamo would allow a proportional reduction of the current needed. "I cannot imagine," Upton said later, "why I did not see the elementary facts in 1878 and 1879 more clearly than I did. I came to Mr. Edison a trained man, with a year's experience at Helmholtz' laboratory . . . a working knowledge of calculus and a mathematical turn of mind. Yet my eyes were blind in comparison with the eyes of today; and . . . I want to say that I had *company!*"

Upton's figures showed Edison the road he must take; and they showed him, too, that even his unique system of electrical distribution was going to require formidable amounts of money simply to create, and even more formidable quantities of cash to put into service. He was going to have to turn to Wall Street for support.

Edison had prepared for that step through a cunning campaign of deliberate publicity-seeking. He had placed an order, when he visited William Wallace on September 8, for a dynamo to use in his experiments; and on September 13 he wired Wallace, "Hurry up the machine. I have struck a big bonanza." The "bonanza," at that point, existed only in Edison's exuberant imagination, but Wallace passed the word around, and within three days a reporter from the New York *Sun* was at Menlo Park for an interview. Edison was in an expansive mood, and declared, "I have it now." On the stock exchanges of the world, the shares of the gas-lighting companies took the first of many steep, sudden plunges. Edison told the *Sun* man,

> Singularly enough, I have obtained it [the light] through an entirely different process than that from which scientists have sought to secure it. They have all been working in the same groove. When it is known how I have accomplished my object everyone will wonder why they never thought of it. . . . I can produce a thousand—aye, ten thousand lights from one machine.

Nor did Edison shield himself from the journalists of the rival papers, the New York *Herald* and the New York *Tribune*. In the *Tribune* for September 28, Edison was quoted as saying there was "no difficulty about dividing up the electric current," though he admitted he was still looking for a good "candle" that would give a pleasant light. "I have let the other inventors get the start of me in this matter . . . but I believe I can catch up to them now."

This sort of talk produced the desired result. The great men of the financial world began to sniff dollars and dividends in Edison's new light. Of course, Edison was far out on a limb with his confident claims. As Upton said, it seemed to many of his men that he was taking too big a risk of embarrassing failure: "I have often thought that Edison got himself into trouble purposely, by premature publication . . . so that he would have a full incentive to get himself out of trouble." But, though Edison may have had qualms in the dark hours of the night about his chances for making good his boasts, he knew that he must have funds to carry forth the research.

Grosvenor Lowrey was the one who had encouraged him to make his rash statements. Lowrey knew that they were necessary to snare the attention of the bankers and stockbrokers. Also at Lowrey's advice, Edison for the first time closed his

103

Menlo Park laboratory to outsiders, so that no one could see the actual state of progress.

At the end of September, 1878, while Edison was still toying with his interruptible platinum coil, Lowrey had a talk with Hamilton M. Twombly, a Western Union director and the son-in-law of the railroad tycoon W. H. Vanderbilt. Lowrey offered Twombly a half interest in the electric light for $150,000. Edison approved of the offer, telling Lowrey, "All I want at present is to be provided with funds enough to push the light rapidly."

On October 2 Lowrey spent an hour and a half in Vanderbilt's Fifth Avenue mansion. He came away with the tentative understanding that Vanderbilt and Twombly would take part in the syndicate of electric-light investors, and that night Lowrey wrote to Edison promising to have "a clear $100,000" soon. Having aroused the interest of the directors of his own company, Western Union, Lowrey next took his tale to the dominant banking firm of the day, Drexel, Morgan & Co. J. Pierpont Morgan, the powerful and awe-inspiring head of Drexel, Morgan wielded, some said, far more authority in the nation than did the President. Lowrey was able to inform Edison that the Morgan interests were inclined to back him. He cautioned the inventor not to get trapped into any other negotiations, and Edison replied, "I shall agree to nothing, promise nothing and say nothing, leaving the whole matter to you."

By October 15, 1878, the first contracts were drawn. A corporation known as the Edison Electric Light Company was formed, with 3000 shares outstanding having a par value of $100 apiece. The group of investors assembled by Lowrey would buy 500 of these shares at par value, for a total amount of $50,000. This money would be paid to Edison in installments in exchange for the rights to all his electric light inventions over the next five years. Edison also would receive without cost the remaining 2500 shares of the company, with a total par value of $250,000. "The objects for which the said company is formed are to own, manufacture, operate and license the use of various apparatus used in producing light, heat and power by electricity," said the articles of incorporation.

The investors included Vanderbilt, Twombly, Lowrey, and three other members of Western Union's board of directors: Norvin Green, Tracy Edson, and James Banker. The seventh member of the syndicate was Eggisto Fabbri, one of Morgan's partners. Morgan himself preferred, for tactical reasons, to keep his own name off the board of directors of Edison Electric Light, but it was understood that Drexel, Morgan & Co. would be the new company's bankers. For their investment of $50,000 in cash, these men obtained a clear title to the work of America's most brilliant inventor as he embarked on his most ambitious enterprise.

What did Edison get in return? For now, $50,000 in cash with which to continue his research. But also, 2500 shares of Edison Electric Light. If the company prospered—as it would, unless his own confidence had been misplaced—the value of those shares would rise enormously, and he would become a millionaire. With Edison as its brains, Morgan as its moneybags, and men like Vanderbilt and Lowrey on the board of directors, how could the company fail?

With the financial arrangements complete, Edison called in the reporters again. On October 20, 1878, his most optimistic statements yet were published in the New York *Sun*. He revealed that he would soon light downtown New York—streets, public buildings, and private residences—with 500,000 incandescent lights.

> Instead of manufacturing all the electricity at one central point, as gas companies make gas, there would be twenty stations. Each station would have an engine and several electric generating agencies. The only thing to be accurately determined is its economy. I am already positive that it will be cheaper than gas, but have not yet determined how

105

much cheaper. To determine its economy, I am now putting up a brick building back of my laboratory here. It is to be 125 feet long. I have already ordered two eighty-horsepower engines for this building. I consider them the best engines in the country. We use no batteries. It isn't necessary. We simply turn the power of steam into electricity, and the greater steam-power we obtain the more electricity we get. One object in putting up this brick building is to ascertain how many electrical jets, each equal to one gas jet, can be obtained from one horsepower.

The task of converting the great city from gas to electric light was no task at all, said Edison.

I think that the engines will be powerful enough to furnish light to all houses within a circle of half a mile. We could lay the wires right through the gas-pipes, and bring them into the houses. All that will be necessary will be to remove the gas burners and substitute electric burners. The light can be regulated by a screw the same as gas. You may have a bright light or not, as you wish. You can turn it down or up, just as you please, and can shut it off at any time. No match is needed to light it. You turn the cock, the electric connection is made, the platinum burner catches a proper degree of heat, and there is your light. There is neither blaze nor flame. There is no singing nor flickering. I don't pretend that it will give a much better light than gas, but it will be whiter and steadier than any known light. . . . It will give no fumes nor smoke. No carbonic-acid gas will be thrown off by combustion. It will be a great thing for compositors, engravers, and all forced to work during hot summer nights, for it will throw out hardly any heat. Shades may be used the same as shades upon gas-lights, but there will be no real necessity for them. The wind can't blow it out. There can be no gas explosions, and no one will be suffocated because the electricity is turned on, for it cannot be turned on without lighting the burner. A person may have lamps made with flexible cords, and carry them from one point to another.

106

Despite Edison's later claim that he had visualized electric meters as part of his original concept, he told this interviewer that he had made

> no attempt to discover a meter. I know that it can be measured, but it may take some time to find out how. I propose that a man pay so much for so many burners, whether he uses them or not. If I find that this works an injustice, why, I shall try to get up a meter, but I fear it will be very hard to do it.

Lastly, Edison displayed the dynamo he had purchased from Wallace. The *Sun* article declared:

> A knot of magnets run around the cylinder facing each other. Wires were attached to it. Edison slipped a belt over the machine, and the engine used in his manufactory began to turn the cylinder. He touched the point of the wire on a small piece of metal near the window casing, and there was a flash of blinding white light. It was repeated at each touch. "There is your steam-power turned into an electric light," he said.

Now he demonstrated the platinum lamp:

> There was the light, clear, cold, and beautiful. The intense brightness was gone. There was nothing irritating to the eye. The mechanism was so simple and perfect that it explained itself. The strip of platinum that acted as burner did not burn. It was incandescent. It threw off a light pure and white. It was set in a gallows-like frame, but it glowed with the phosphorescent effulgence of the star Altair. You could trace the veins in your hands and the spots and lines upon your fingernails by its brightness. All the surplus electricity had been turned off, and the platinum shone with a mellow radiance through the small glass globe that surrounded it. A turn of the screw, and its brightness became dazzling, or was reduced to the faintest glimmer of a glowworm. The professor [Edison] gazed at it with pride.

The professor was quick to turn the phosphorescent effulgence off, though. If he had let the lamp burn more than a few minutes, it would have embarrased him by going out.

Each new report of Edison's incandescent wonders had its immediate effect on the stock market. From London came word that, "owing to the publication of Professor Edison's discovery of the distribution of electric light," all gaslight securities had dropped in value by some 12 per cent within a few days. The gas companies of New York City, already harried by destructive price wars among themselves, showed even more severe declines. A proposed Brush arc light system for New York threatened to take away the 10 per cent of their income that came from street lighting, and now Edison Electric Light appeared about to grab the rest. In six weeks that autumn, Manhattan Gas Light stock fell from 187½ to 147½, Metropolitan Gas Light from 132½ to 106½, New York Gas Light from 92½ to 80, Mutual Gas Light from 74½ to 60, Municipal Gas Light from 97½ to 85, and Harlem Gas Light from 72½ to 39.

Rumors flew wildly about. It was said that other inventors, less inclined toward publicity than Edison, were far ahead of the Wizard of Menlo Park in the race toward perfecting the incandescent lamp. In England, Joseph Swan was indeed well along with a carbon-rod vacuum lamp that he hoped to demonstrate publicly early in 1879. St. George Lane-Fox, another English inventor, took out a patent in 1878 for an incandescent lamp with a platinum-iridium alloy. Closer at hand, an American telegrapher named William E. Sawyer applied for a patent at the end of October, 1878, showing an incandescent lamp with a short pencil-shaped rod of carbon in an atmosphere of nitrogen. Sawyer's partner was Albion Man, a Brooklyn lawyer who provided financial and some technical assistance. They claimed to have tried platinum already and found it wanting, and insisted that they had "beaten" Edison to a workable lamp. News of the Sawyer-Man electric light stirred panic among Edison

108

Electric Light's uneasy stockholders. They suggested buying up Sawyer's patents to choke off competition. On November 1, 1878, Edison vetoed the notion.

A letter to Lowrey from Edison's secretary, S. L. Griffin, made his position clear. "He was visibly agitated," wrote Griffin, "and said it was the old story, that is lack of confidence—the same experience he had had with the telephone, and in fact, all of his successful inventions, was being re-enacted! No combination, no consolidation for him." Edison, through Griffin, emphasized that "the *line he was developing was entirely original and out of the rut.*" Talk of purchasing the Sawyer-Man light subsided.

Next came stories that Edison was seriously ill, and that he had been refused a patent by the British Patent Office for his platinum light. Grosvenor Lowrey wrote to the New York *Tribune* in mid-November to spike these tales:

Dear Sir,

Your columns this morning contain the following, which you will undoubtedly be glad to correct:

"It is understood that Mr. Edison is suffering from ill-health, and has given up his experiments with the electric light."

My relation to Mr. Edison in respect to his inventions and discoveries in electric lighting gives me opportunity to know the truth about these matters, and the public interest concerning them makes it seem a duty to correct statements which I know to be erroneous. Mr. Edison's ill-health, I learn indirectly from his family physician, Dr. Leslie Ward, and directly from Dr. E. L. Keyes, who visited him professionally two weeks ago at Menlo Park, was of a temporary character and not at all serious. For two weeks past Mr. Edison has been daily and nightly, as usual, at work in his laboratory upon the electric light. I spent several hours with him a few days since. He seemed in the highest spirits and in excellent health, and very enthusiastic over the results of his work in electric lighting. . . .

His first invention, as it will appear in the first patents to be issued, will but inadequately show the novel discoveries and devices which he has made even to this time, when, according to his own views, he is comparatively only upon the threshold of a new and wonderful development of electrical science. In the meantime, the proper exhibition of what has already been invented, as well as the study of the economical questions involved, require the erection of large buildings, etc., which is now going on with the utmost rapidity. Pending their completion Mr. Edison, far from having given up his experiments, is pursuing the great variety of them with his customary energy and even more than his customary good fortune.

In the meantime there is an interest somewhere to set on foot false reports affecting Mr. Edison's light, one of which, recently circulated in an up-town club, I beg space to correct. It was stated that an official paper emanating from the British Patent Office had been seen which denied a patent to Mr. Edison. The author of the report would, perhaps, have been more careful had he known that the legal period fixed for the issue or denial of such a patent has not yet been reached, and that the existence of such a paper at this time is, therefore, impossible.

Lowrey's letter, like Edison's grandiose statements of September and October, was compounded of equal quantities of wishful thinking, deliberate overoptimism, and justified confidence. But now the weeks were passing, and little of note was coming from the workshop at Menlo Park. The skeptical mutterings grew louder, particularly after the texts of Edison's first patent applications became available in the United States and Great Britain. Silvanus P. Thompson, a British authority on dynamo design, gave a public lecture on "The Electric Light" at Bristol on November 8, in which he said,

> I cannot tell you what Mr. Edison's particular method of distributing the current to the spirals may be, but this I can tell you as the result of all experience, that any system of lighting by incandescence will utterly fail from an economic point of view, and will be the more uneconomical the more the light is subdivided.

110

In the United States, the *Scientific News* for November 1 remarked,

> We do not know, of course, what science may be able to achieve in the line of giving us a cheap and effective light, for as yet we do not know what Edison has discovered, but we do say that no published discovery in the electric light need cause any anxiety to gas-producers, so far as it may be applicable to general uses.

A similar comment came from a contemporary English journal:

> All anxiety concerning the Edison light may be put on one side. It is certainly not going to take the place of gas, and its invention would not have been regarded with the anxiety and interest which have been displayed had it not been for the statements of newspaper reporters on the other side of the Atlantic. In the whole specification we have not one word concerning any new or extraordinary contrivance for dividing the electric light.

Even the *Scientific American,* usually sympathetic to Edison, found it necessary to publish this stern warning in its issue of February 15, 1879:

> The Philadelphia *Bulletin* suggests that if Mr. Edison wishes public faith in that electric light of his to remain steadfast, he will have to give an early demonstration of the truth of his claim that it is a practical success. When he first announced that he had solved the problem of dividing the light and adapting it to domestic uses, there was a very general inclination to accept the story with absolute confidence because Mr. Edison had proved by his previous inventions that he could achieve some things which had been regarded by other men as impossible. But, after all, the proof of the pudding is in the eating, and the world, after waiting patiently for the public display of an invention

111

which sent gas stocks down as soon as it was heralded, will be disposed, unless Mr. Edison shows his hand, to suspect that the Edison Electric Light and the Keely Motor [a perpetual-motion machine] will have to be ranked together as enterprises which contained more of promise than of performance.

Possibly the most unsettling criticism of all came from a London newspaper whose scientific correspondent had gone carefully over Edison's platinum-lamp patent application. He declared:

> This document reveals for the first time authoritatively the line on which Edison is experimenting. It reveals nothing new, however, for in one manner and another the substantial facts in regard to Edison's experiments had all been obtained previously. The Edison lamp, it appears, is a piece of metal which may be platinum, rhodium, titanium, ormium, or any other very infusible metal fashioned into a coil, helix, ribbon, plate, or any other form, and made incandescent. The current is regulated by a metal bar through which it passes. This bar expands when the current is too strong, and shunts or short-circuits the flow of electricity. Or it may be regulated by the operation of a diaphragm which is acted upon by the expansion of the air or gas enclosed in a tube. This is all that Edison's specification aims at, so far as the apparatus of the lamp is concerned, and scientific men may judge for themselves as to the probable success of the Edison light. The weak point of the lamp is this, that in order to be luminous, platinum must be heated almost to the point of melting. With a slight increase in the current, the lamp melts in the twinkling of an eye, and in practice the regulator is found to short-circuit the current too late to prevent the damage. It is this difficulty which must be overcome. Can it be done?

That question was troubling Edison, too, as winter descended on Menlo Park:

Can it be done?

112

seven

In Quest of a Filament

A HIGH-RESISTANCE burner: that was the answer. Upton's calculations of late November, 1878, had showed that clearly, confirming Edison's own intuition.

Different substances vary in their electrical resistances. An inch-thick rod of copper, for example, has a far lower resistance than an inch-thick rod of the same length made of iron or lead. The thickness of the cross-section is also important in determining resistance; wires of the same metal and the same length have resistances inversely proportional to the areas of their cross-sections. Edison's requirements called for some substance of naturally high resistance and high melting point. His burner would need to have a very thin cross-section, he now saw—to be little more than a thread, in fact. A thin burner, having a higher resistance and far less heat-radiating surface than a thick burner of the same substance, would require much less current to reach incandescence. So, to describe his burner, Edison adopted the word "filament" from the Latin *filare*, "to spin."

In January of 1879, still using platinum for his burner, Edison designed his first high-resistance lamp. He used a long, thin platinum wire, winding it closely (to reduce its radiating sur-

113

face) around a clay spool. To keep the wire from oxidizing he coated it with zirconium oxide. This lamp, too, had a heat-governed regulator, which opened the lamp's circuit instead of short-circuiting the burner as before. Edison had seen that short-circuiting the burner would short-circuit the generator too, if, as he now intended, he wired his lamps in parallel.

Using his simple air pump, he created the best vacuum he could get within the bulb, and turned on the current. The lamp burned for several hours. That was encouraging. But perhaps some other filament material would give better results. Edison began one of his familiar quests, trying everything that happened to fit the qualifications: chromium, molybdenum, osmium, boron, silicon, and so on. A thin wire of nickel produced a brilliant light—so brilliant that Edison's notebook entry for January 27, 1879 reads, "Owing to the enormous power of the light my eyes commenced to pain after seven hours' work, and I had to quit." A day later he wrote, "Suffered the pains of hell with my eyes last night from 10 P.M. to 4 A.M. when got to sleep with a dose of morphine. Eyes getting better. . . ."

Shortly he was back to platinum again, but with a new approach. Belatedly Edison had learned of the Sprengel mercury vacuum pump, invented in 1865. It was Sir William Crookes's use of this pump ten years later that had inspired Joseph Swan to resume his experiments with incandescent bulbs. Edison knew little or possibly nothing of Swan's work, which was continuing at that moment on lines nearly parallel to his own. But when he heard that a Sprengel pump had reached the College of New Jersey (now Princeton University), he sent Francis Upton off to borrow it.

The mathematician set out for Princeton by train and buggy, did some glib talking, and returned late at night to Menlo Park with the precious pump. Edison was waiting up for him. So fascinating was the pump that Edison insisted on going to work immediately, keeping his men pumping until dawn. The pump produced a satisfyingly high vacuum, yielding the brightest and most long-lived platinum light thus far.

In the course of his work with the Sprengel pump, Edison made an interesting discovery about platinum: the metal tended to become very hard after it had been heated two or three times by a current. Why? Edison reasoned correctly that there must be gas in the pores of the filament which is driven out by the heat of incandescence. Using the pump, Edison succeeded in releasing these "occluded" gases from the platinum filament without burning out the wire; the gas-free filament now was much sturdier and better able to resist the effects of heat. It could be operated safely at higher temperatures, producing a brighter light.

The better the vacuum, Edison knew, the longer the filament would last. With the aid of his skilled glass blowers, he devised techniques for sealing his bulbs around the burner while still connected to the pump. The results were rewarding. At last he felt he was on the right track. On April 12, 1879, he drew up his initial patent application for a high-resistance platinum lamp.

Meanwhile the competition was making headway. Joseph Swan had displayed an incandescent lamp at Newcastle on December 18, 1878, though he had not attempted to light it then. But when he lectured before the Philosophical Society of Newcastle the following February, Swan made a successful demonstration of the lighted lamp. It had a carbon burner and was enclosed in a glass globe that had been pumped free of air with the Sprengel pump. At once there was talk of a system of Swan lights for Newcastle. In the United States, the Brush arc lights were about to be installed in Cleveland, and other cities were showing interest. Edison's uneasy sponsors began to fret. It was not so much that they feared losing their trifling $50,000 investment; Edison was demanding more money to continue his work, and they had no idea how much cash the project would devour before something came of it.

115

In seven months Edison had spent nearly all that had been given him. Platinum sold for $5 an ounce, and he burned it up as though it grew on bushes at Menlo Park. Even after his basic capital expenditures, such as that of the dynamo, were out of the way, his costs were running at $400 a week. He decided to electrify the region within a half-mile radius about Menlo Park, and discovered that it would require $18,000 in copper wiring alone. Where was the money to come from?

For the benefit of the newspapers Edison was unfailingly optimistic. He had, he said, a "nearly perfect vacuum," and had virtually perfected both his lamp and his circuitry. Little remained but to find a source of cheap platinum; and he had no doubt that this hitherto scarce metal could somehow be obtained in quantity. With an eye toward publicity, Edison hired a band of prospectors and turned them loose in the Rockies to find him a platinum mine. Professor Barker, perturbed, warned him against the "indiscriminate examination of rocks," and even the loyal Lowrey thought the search was foredoomed. The stockholders continued to grumble.

Just about the time Edison was filing his April 12 patent application, the directors of Edison Electric Light held a critical meeting. There was talk of pulling out to prevent further losses. Lowrey eloquently begged them to be patient, saying, "We must all stand by the inventor and the enterprise." J. P. Morgan, who was present, remained ominously silent a long while. Finally he expressed a willingness to give Edison a little more time.

Lowrey suggested to Edison that he come to New York, see Morgan, and reassure the great banker. Coolly, Edison replied that he was too busy to leave Menlo Park; let Morgan come to *him*. Morgan, surprisingly, agreed. On a bleak, raw day in mid-April, a group of the world's wealthiest men boarded a late afternoon train for New Jersey to see Edison's high-resistance platinum lamp.

It was already dark when they arrived. Edison conducted

116

them into the machine shop, where several platinum lamps were mounted, and then quickly took them on into his library without demonstrating anything. For half an hour he explained the nature of his experiments and discussed his results, while his impatient guests fidgeted. Building the suspense with a masterly hand, Edison at length led Morgan, Lowrey, and the others across the yard into the laboratory to show them pieces of platinum wire and to point out the arrangements of lights on brackets along the wall. He spoke of the powerful Gramme dynamo that would soon replace the Wallace machine he had used up to now. At last it was quite dark. Edison ordered John Kruesi to "turn on the juice slowly."

The power came on, and the lamps began to glow cherry-red. Edison signalled for more current, and more, until the brilliance was awesome. Then one bulb glittered with fatal brightness. There was a quick puff and all the lights went out; for Edison had not yet been able to wire his lamps in parallel, and when one burned out, all went. Charles Batchelor quickly found the burned-out lamp and replaced it with a new one. Again the current was turned up, again the lamps glowed pleasantly—and again one failed. Two or three times the group was plunged into sudden darkness.

Edison explained that until he had a certain type of constant-voltage dynamo, he could not wire the lamps properly. Just now, for the purposes of the demonstration, they were wired in series, which was why the whole board darkened when one lamp failed. This technical explanation did not satisfy the financiers. They could not follow Edison's talk of circuitry, but they could see quite plainly that the lamps were going out. Their mood was grim as they left Menlo Park that evening.

They were willing to put up more money for Edison, but their hopes were faint. Inevitably, word leaked on Wall Street that the Morgan group was disappointed in Edison's progress thus far. The stock of Edison Electric Light, which had risen as high as $600 a share, fell badly, while the suffering gas stocks

117

began to recover. William Sawyer triumphantly told the New York *Herald* on April 27 that Edison's newest lamp patent showed "nothing new," and that his attempts were destined for "final, necessary, and ignominious failure."

Edison himself was dismayed by the demonstration. Brooding over the anticlimactic disaster, he decided that the platinum filament was fundamentally unsuitable. Even at its best it would not be good enough for large-scale use, since it was too costly, too unreliable. He ordered a general housecleaning at Menlo Park. The platinum lamps went into storage, and the search for a filament began anew.

His early optimism, which had not entirely been a calculated public facade, remained strong. But now he knew that the problem he had tackled was far more difficult than he had supposed. He had quite seriously believed, the previous September, that he would master the electric light in "about six weeks." Now he was in his eighth month of dogged work, with a long way to go. He remarked in an 1890 interview,

> Just consider this. We have an almost infinitesimal filament heated to a degree which it is difficult to comprehend, and it is in a vacuum under conditions of which we are wholly ignorant. You cannot use your eyes to help you, and you really know nothing of what is going on in that tiny bulb. I speak without exaggeration when I say that I have constructed 3,000 different theories in connection with the electric light, each of them reasonable and apparently likely to be true. Yet in two cases only did my experiments prove the truth of my theories.

During spring and early summer he tried a variety of substances for the filament. Platinum remained a constant temptation, and he continued to go back to it despite his insight of mid-April that it could not work. On July 7, 1879, in a progress report to Tracy Edson, one of the original Edison Electric Light stockholders, Edison confidently announced that he expected a

118

plentiful supply of platinum and zirconium oxide to be available. "Everything looks bright," he said. He was learning new ways of handling the Sprengel pump, and by late summer had managed to obtain a vacuum of one one-millionth of an atmosphere within his glass globes. But everything was not bright. The platinum lamps were as unreliable as ever. He could not find an adequate and low-priced stock of platinum. Even the zirconium oxide coating was hard to come by. "I shall give up the use of zircon," he told one of his mineral suppliers on August 21. A notebook entry for October 8 complained, "At this date the trouble is to get an insulation for the platinum wire. . . . All known oxides are to be tried."

Then, abruptly and finally, he cast platinum aside once more. Sometime in early October of 1879 he settled on carbon for his filament—thus returning to the material with which he had begun the quest more than a year before. Carbon had been unsatisfactory then, when he had used it in low-resistance bulbs. But now he could create a much more complete vacuum within the bulb, and he understood how to produce incandescence with relatively little current. Moreover, his work with platinum had showed him how to make a filament heat-resistant by driving out the occluded gases.

So carbon it would be. A story told by nearly all of Edison's early biographers credits the inspiration to chance. As Francis Arthur Jones related it in a 1907 biography:

> Thirteen months had passed, thirteen months of tireless investigation, and at last Edison became convinced that he was on the wrong track. Platinum and all metals must be abandoned. But what was left? He was groping about in search of a fingerpost that should point to the right path, and he couldn't find one. And then the secret was suddenly revealed to him in a way which clearly indicated that Nature, having enjoyed her year's sport, had at last made up her mind to reward the sturdy investigator for his courage by acting generously towards him. . . .

119

The inventor was seated in his laboratory alone one evening, a little serious over his thousand-and-one disappointments, though by no means crushed in spirit, and, as usual, thinking deeply, when his right hand, which lay idly upon the table, strayed towards a little pile of lampblack mixed with tar which his assistants had been using in connection with his telephone transmitter. Picking up a modicum of this substance he began rolling it between his finger and thumb, still wondering what one thing he had forgotten which should make the electric light possible, and little dreaming that it lay between his fingers. For perhaps half an hour he continued to ponder and at the same time to roll the mixture, until at last he had obtained a thin thread not unlike a piece of wire in appearance. He looked at it idly, and then began to speculate on its possibilities as a filament for an incandescent lamp. It was carbon, of course, and, this being so, might have strength to withstand the electric current to a greater degree than platinum itself. He determined to put it to the test, and at once began the work of rolling out fine threads of the black composition preparatory to placing them in the lamps.

The truth is probably more prosaic, involving less sudden inspiration, more careful thought. Edison was always a conscious craftsman who operated by steady and exhaustive research rather than depending on thunderbolts from on high. He had always known carbon's merits. Alas, he had also discovered carbon's defects in the late summer of 1878. But in the months that followed he had mastered new techniques, and with platinum so clearly unacceptable, it was reasonable to apply those new techniques to the earlier material.

Edison's own notebooks give the lie to the legend of the dejected inventor seizing upon carbon at the last moment when all else had failed him. The October 8 notebook entry shows him still working on a platinum lamp; the notebook also shows that Edison simultaneously had been systematically testing various kinds of carbon filament since the summer. He began by mixing lampblack with tar to give it a puttylike resilience, and winding the stuff into spiral coils, either by squirting it through a die or by rolling it with a piece of wood. These coils, when baked, gave adequate light for an hour or two. A notebook entry for October 7 declares, "A spiral made of burnt lampblack was even better than the Wallace (soft carbon) mixture."

His calculations showed that the carbon filament should be no more than a sixty-fourth of an inch in diameter to have the proper high-resistance characteristic. Swan, at just about the same time, was constructing lamps with a carbon filament a sixth of an inch thick, which required vastly much more current. It was an arduous job to draw the tar-and-lampblack mixture into such fine threads, but Edison and his team, working virtually round the clock and pausing only for brief naps, learned how to make threadlike filaments only seven one-thousandths of an inch in diameter by mid-October. But they were enormously fragile. Batchelor, Edison's "hands," had an almost supernatural skill at mounting the tiny filaments, keeping eyes and fingers steady for hours. All too often, however, the filaments broke before they could be tested. Edison decided to look for some sturdier form of carbon.

Carbonized sewing thread seemed a likely possibility. They packed pieces of thread in an earthenware crucible and covered them with powdered carbon. The crucible was cemented shut and placed in a furnace at a high temperature for several hours. When it had cooled, each charred thread was carefully wired to the stem assembly of a lamp and enclosed in a glass globe. The vacuum pump was used to exhaust the globe, and the current was turned on. A low current drove the occluded gases from the filament. Then further pumping brought the globe to near-vacuum conditions, and it was sealed and ready for testing.

On the first eight tries, the carbonized thread broke before the lamp could be tested. Edison described the agonizing process many years later in these words:

> All night Batchelor, my assistant, worked beside me. The next day and the next night again, and at the end of that time we had produced one carbon out of an entire spool of Clarke's thread. Having made it, it was necessary to take it to the glass-blower's house. With the utmost precaution Batchelor took up the precious carbon, and I marched after him, as if guarding a mighty treasure. To our consternation, just as we reached the glass-blower's bench the wretched carbon broke. We turned back to the main laboratory and set to work again. It was late in the afternoon before we had produced another carbon, which was again broken by a jeweller's screwdriver falling against it. But we turned back again, and before night the carbon was completed and inserted in the lamp. The bulb was exhausted of air and sealed, the current turned on, and the sight we had so long desired to see met our eyes.

This was the famous Number 9 lamp—the one that marked Edison's success with the incandescent lamp. Curiously, the timetable of triumph is marred by confusion and contradiction. Supposedly the celebrated lamp burned for forty hours or more before it went out. The day of success, everyone agrees, was October 21, 1879. But was that the day when the forty-hour test began, or was it the day that it concluded? Some say that the Number 9 model was turned on during the evening of October 19 and died on October 21. Others have written that the lamp first glowed on the 21st, which means it must have gone on burning until the 23rd.

Edison's own accounts add to the mystery. Probably the most reliable record is in Edison's Menlo Park notebook, which clearly states:

> Oct. 21—No. 9 ordinary thread Coats Co. cord No. 29, came up to one-half candle and was put on 18 cells battery

permanently at 1:30 A.M. No. 9 on from 1:30 A.M. till 3 P.M.
—13½ hours and then was raised to 3 gas jets for one hour
then cracked glass and busted.

That gives us an incandescent lamp burning for some fourteen
and one half hours, beginning and ending on October 21. But
Edison also told the story this way:

> We built the lamp and turned on the current. It lit up,
> and in the first few breathless minutes we measured its
> resistance quickly and found it was 275 ohms—all we
> wanted. Then we sat down and looked at that lamp. We
> wanted to see how long it would burn. The problem was
> solved—if the filament would last. The day was—let me see
> —October 21, 1879. We sat and looked, and the lamp con-
> tinued to burn, and the longer it burned the more fascinated
> we were. None of us could go to bed, and there was no
> sleep for any of us for forty hours. We sat and just watched
> it with anxiety growing into elation. It lasted about forty-
> five hours, and then I said, "If it will burn that number of
> hours now, I know I can make it burn a hundred."

When did this lamp burn, if the notebooks speak only of
fourteen and one half hours of successful light? Had Edison
magnified his own greatest moment through some trick of
memory? It would seem that way—except that Batchelor,
Upton, Kruesi, and the three other men who were present that
night also spoke of a "death watch" lasting some forty hours
before the lamp failed. Upton, in fact, fell ill during the experiment, went home to sleep, came back, and found the others still
eagerly staring at the feeble red glow. So perhaps, in the excitement of the moment, something went awry with Edison's
meticulous record-keeping; or perhaps the two-day-long "death
watch" never really happened.

In any case, even a fourteen and one half hour lamp was far
beyond anything that had been achieved before, and, the notebook tells us, it burned out only when the current was raised

past the filament's expected level of tolerance. A basic principle had been established, for here was a lamp of long life that had no regulators, no diaphragms or expansion rods, none of the complex adornments of Edison's platinum lamps. It was simply a cotton thread through which current could pass; and there was every reason to think that success was at hand.

This time Edison sent out no jubilant bulletins to the press. He did not even inform the directors of Edison Electric Light. After a day's rest he was back in the laboratory to confirm his victory and move on to the next stage.

He cracked open the burned-out Number 9 lamp and examined its valiant filament under a microscope. Its structure had changed in use; it was much harder, its fibers tightly compressed. Edison saw that he could improve on his charred-thread filament by finding some fibrous material that would not break so easily while the lamp was being assembled. He gave orders to test everything in sight.

The notebook for October 27, 1879 declares:

> I carbonized the following substances in closed tube at red heat:—
> 1. Vulcanized fibre
> 2. Celluloid
> 3. Boxwood shavings
> 4. Cocoa nut hair and shell
> 5. Drawing paper no. 1
> 6. Architects drawing paper
> 7. Drawing paper sample 30-3
> 8. Drawing paper sample 3
> 9. Spruce shavings
> 10. Hickory shavings
> 11. Baywood shavings
> 12. Cedar (Red) shavings
> 13. Rosewood

14. Fish line
15. Maple shavings
16. Tissue paper string
17. Cotton lampwick
18. Punk
19. Cork
20. Bagging flax

Nor did he stop there. He spied the thick red beard of one of his laboratory assistants, J. U. Mackenzie, and insisted on trying a few of its hairs! Gaily Edison snipped off a sample of Mackenzie's beard, carbonized it, and brought it to incandescence. It worked well enough, but Edison doubted that it really had commercial possibilities.

Before long he came full circle, and returned to the very first material he had used: carbonized paper. Strips of tough cardboard, carbonized and reduced to thin filaments, proved to be just the thing. They burned as long as one hundred and seventy hours, and Edison was sure he could get his paper filaments to give up to a thousand hours of light. On November 1, 1879, he composed a patent application on his carbon filament lamp, filing it three days later. This patent, which was granted on January 27, 1880, was the cornerstone of Edison's electrical system, to be followed by 168 later electric light patents. He declared:

Be it known that I, THOMAS ALVA EDISON of Menlo Park, in the State of New Jersey, United States of America, have invented an Improvement in Electric Lamps, and in the method of manufacturing the same . . . of which the following is a specification.

The object of this invention is to produce electric lamps giving light by incandescence, which lamps shall have high resistance, so as to allow of the practical subdivision of the electric light.

The invention consists in a light-giving body of carbon wire

125

or sheets coiled or arranged in such a manner as to offer great resistance to the passage of the electric current, and at the same time present but a slight surface from which radiation can take place.

The invention further consists in placing such burner of great resistance in a nearly-perfect vacuum, to prevent oxidation and injury to the conductor by the atmosphere. The current is conducted into the vacuum-bulb through platina wires sealed into the glass.

The invention further consists in the method of manufacturing carbon conductors of high resistance, so as to be suitable for giving light by incandescence, and in the manner of securing perfect contact between the metallic conductors or leading-wires and the carbon conductor.

The application reviewed the disadvantages of such incandescent lights as had been developed prior to his:

. . . rods of carbon of one to four ohms resistance, placed in closed vessels, in which the atmospheric air has been replaced by gases that do not combine chemically with the carbon.

After speaking of the unsuitability of such bulbs, Edison made his chief claim:

I have discovered that even a cotton thread properly carbonized and placed in a sealed glass bulb exhausted to one-millionth of an atmosphere offers from one hundred to five hundred ohms resistance to the passage of the current, and that it is absolutely stable at very high temperatures. . . .

There followed a technical description of the making of the filament and its attachment to the wires that carried the current. Finally Edison summarized his work:

I claim as my invention—
1. An electric lamp for giving light by incandescence, consisting of a filament of carbon of high resistance, made as described, and secured to metallic wires, as set forth.

126

2. The combination of carbon filaments with a receiver made entirely of glass and conductors passing through the glass, and from which receiver the air is exhausted, for the purposes set forth.

3. A carbon filament or strip coiled and connected to electric conductors so that only a portion of the surface of such carbon conductors shall be exposed for radiating light, as set forth.

4. The method herein described of securing the platina contact-wires to the carbon filament and carbonizing of the whole in a closed chamber, substantially as set forth.

Signed by me this 1st day of November, A.D. 1879.

THOMAS A. EDISON

Witnesses:

S. L. GRIFFIN,
JOHN F. RANDOLPH

eight

Bamboos
and
Dynamos

THE way now was clear. Edison had vaulted past everyone else in the field of incandescent lighting. The Sawyer-Man lamp, which in its latest form used a carbonized paper strip in a nitrogen atmosphere, was unsatisfactory; the nitrogen aided the destructive vaporization of the carbon. Joseph Swan had built a durable carbon rod lamp, but it was of the low-resistance type and devoured a hundred times as much current as Edison's, so it was hardly suitable for commercial use. St. George Lane-Fox was the only man besides Edison who had experimented with high-resistance lamps, but his lamp did not function effectively. Edison, building on the mistakes of his predecessors, had created something new and valuable.

The gas burners in the Menlo Park laboratory were replaced with electric lights. Edison also had the new lights installed in his Menlo Park home, as did Francis Upton. Early in November, 1879, Egisto Fabbri and another Morgan partner visited Menlo Park and saw the lamps in use.

They were pleased, but not overly jubilant. Whatever delight they may have taken in the sight of the glowing lamps was tempered by Edison's request for more money. He wanted an advance of some thousands of dollars to build a pilot power station that would electrify all of Menlo Park. But the financiers, having carried him thus far, hesitated. They had seen him develop the phonograph, then lose interest in it, call it "a mere toy," and put it aside. What if he lost interest in electric lights after consuming nearly $100,000 in advances from the stockholders? At the moment of triumph it seemed that timidity would prevail.

Grosvenor Lowrey once more came to the rescue. The invention, he told the board of directors, was of "enormous value." He declared ringingly, "Edison is giving us the greatest return for capital that was ever offered—his talent, his knowledge, his health—while plenty of others [give] only capital." Lowrey persuaded them to disgorge a small sum, enough to let Edison build his Menlo Park installation. The inventor was annoyed by their close-fisted way with him.

For Edison, Lowrey had a bold suggestion: give a public demonstration of the electric light! Edison was uneasy. It seemed too soon to show the public what he had done. But Lowrey, that shrewd promoter, knew what he was doing. An open display of the new light would stir a great clamor among the citizens—and the startled cries of the public would move Edison's frugal capitalists to put up more funds for the work. How soon, Lowrey wanted to know, could Edison offer his display? What about New Year's Eve? What a fine way to usher in 1880! Edison, swept along by his friend's enthusiasm, agreed to stage a public showing of the incandescent lamp on December 31.

Now began a time of furious preparation at Menlo Park. Workmen toiled to get one hundred of the paper-filament lamps ready within the next six weeks. Edison and his lieutenants drew their plans for wiring the town.

All during the thirteen-month campaign for a usable lamp, Edison had simultaneously been engaged with the other aspects

129

of a generating and transmitting system—not to mention such external affairs as the patent wrangle over his telephone speaker, which had gone on at exactly this time. His concern extended to every aspect of electricity, not merely to the perfection of an incandescent lamp, and the drama of the lamp tends to obscure the equally significant drama of the dynamo.

Edison had begun his electrical research using a small dynamo made for him by William Wallace. In the late spring of 1879, when Edison Electric Light funds were at his disposal, he replaced it with a larger Gramme machine. But Edison had already realized that the best existing dynamos were hopelessly inefficient; he would have to invent his own.

He had studied the report of Professors Thomson and Houston to the Franklin Institute of Philadelphia late in 1878. Their rating gave the Gramme dynamo a generating efficiency of 38 to 41 per cent, the Brush dynamo 31 per cent, the Wallace dynamo somewhat less. Most of the current generated in these machines was wasted uselessly in heating the generator's coils. That might be acceptable for powering arc lights in series circuits; it would never do for what Edison had in mind. He wanted a dynamo that would be 60 per cent efficient, at the very least.

By the theory of the day such a dynamo was innately impossible. Experts held that the internal resistance of a dynamo had to be equal to its external resistance, so that the maximum conceivable efficiency could be no more than 50 per cent. As early as December of 1878, Edison had decided that this rule simply did not hold true for a properly constructed dynamo. According to the memoirs of Francis Jehl, a law clerk in Lowrey's office who had become a Menlo Park laboratory assistant early in 1879, Edison

> did not intend to build up a system of distribution in which the external resistance would be equal to the internal resistance. He said he was just about going to do the *opposite*;

130

he wanted a large external resistance and a low internal resistance. He said he wanted to sell the energy outside the station and not waste it in the dynamo and the conductors, where it brought no profits. . . .

Calculating resistances and voltages, a task that fell to Upton and Jehl, was no trivial task. Instruments for measuring volts, amperes, and ohms did not yet exist; the term "ampere" had not even been coined in 1879. Said Jehl, "it was like a carpenter without his foot rule." But they managed. Edison had learned a great deal about electromagnets during his years in telegraphy, and he put that knowledge to good use now.

He abandoned the fashionable ring-wound design of the Gramme machine, adopting a variant of the more advanced drum armature developed in Germany. Instead of using solid armature cores, as was customary, Edison devised laminated cores—that is, he had them made of thin sheets of iron, insulated from each other though mounted on a single shaft. These cores, Edison predicted, would produce less heat than solid ones, and would not tend to generate the wasteful "eddy currents" of the Brush and Gramme dynamos. The invaluable Upton covered many sheets of paper with equations before Edison's original concept was transformed into a reality; John Kruesi built the actual cores from Upton's blueprints.

The magnets of the Edison dynamo were unusually large, and gave the machine an instantly distinct and recognizable form. They were 3½ feet tall, rising in a pair on each dynamo and joined at the top by an iron crosspiece, to form a shape like that of the Greek capital letter *pi* (π). The twin magnets jutting up from the squat drum of the base gave the dynamo its nickname, "Long-waisted Mary Ann."

It was an awkward-looking machine, far from flawless in design. But when Kruesi's first working model was tested in back of the Menlo Park engine house, the results surprised even Edison. Long-waisted Mary Ann was 90 per cent efficient in

131

converting steam power into electrical energy! She would produce a constant voltage of 110 volts, as Edison intended, and even when power demands were stepped up the voltage fell only slightly. Edison knew that there was scope for improvement in his dynamo, since it still created fairly high internal resistance and wasted some of its energy in the form of heat, but minor technical adjustments over the next few years could —and did—take care of that. The important thing was that he had a source of current which, while based entirely on existing technical knowledge, was two to three times as efficient as any that had ever been built before.

The Long-waisted Mary Ann—or, as Edison himself preferred to call it, the "Faradic Machine"—was announced officially in the October 18, 1879 *Scientific American*. Upton was the author of the unsigned article. Such a constant-voltage, high-efficiency dynamo seemed incredible to most technical men. Edison who had not yet made good on his boast of perfecting an incandescent lamp was already the butt of considerable ridicule. (He was within three days of success there, of course, but no one knew that yet.) His dynamo seemed a mere fantasy. One scientist insisted that it was impossible to have achieved such results without "destroying the doctrine of the conservation and correlation of forces." Edward Weston, an inventor and dynamo manufacturer from Newark, scoffed at the "Faradic Machine" in the November 1 *Scientific American,* calling it "more or less like a perpetual-motion machine."

Yet it worked, as Edison proposed to show the world on New Year's Eve. Kruesi was given the job of constructing three of the twin-columned dynamos, each capable of delivering 6 kilowatts of electrical energy. They were to be driven by belts running from the steam engine in the machine shop. Lowrey sent a gang of Western Union linemen out to Menlo Park to set up poles and string the overhead power lines for the demonstration.

On dark December afternoons, homeward-bound commuters stared from their train windows as they passed Menlo Park and were astonished to see festoons of small, bright, attractive electric lights strung from building to building. Edison's neighbors came to peer, and told stories of lights blazing brilliantly all night in the laboratory yard. Edison had not yet made an official announcement either of the success of his research or of the December 31 demonstration, but as the work of stringing the outdoor lights continued it was impossible to prevent rumors from circulating. Bizarre stories were told of the "lights strung on wires at Menlo Park." When a particularly bright star appeared in the night sky over America, someone circulated the fable that Edison had put it there, and it was necessary to issue formal denials that the star was actually an Edison light mounted to a balloon.

The gas companies quaked in apprehension. For a full year they had lived with the Edison threat, sighing in relief whenever some learned journal declared the Menlo Park work a failure. Now something ominous seemed to be upon them. The disastrous price wars of 1878 and 1879, brought on by the unethical granting of competing franchises, had already weakened the New York City gas companies severely. The price of gas to lighting customers, which had been $2.25 per thousand cubic feet in 1877, was down to a dollar now. And here came Edison's mysterious light, apparently a reality, with the New York gas companies already marked as his first victims.

The December rumors sent the price of gas stocks tumbling once again. As before, shares in Edison Electric Light went climbing. Only a small quantity of Edison Electric Light stock was available on the open market. Most of the original investors were holding fast, although a few, including Edison, had sold a minor part of their shares. Now the speculators bid frantically for those shares. The price soared to $500 a share, to $1000, to $3500. At the peak of the boom the shares were advancing in value by $100 an hour. Eventually they posted a high price of $8000 a share before dropping back to a more sedate, though still impressive, $5000. Edison, who still held some 2000 shares, was worth $10,000,000 at that point—on paper. But he paid little heed to that.

When the excitement over Edison's light had reached its most frenzied moment, Edison, with magnificent timing, at last made a statement to the press. He called in his friend Marshall Fox and gave him a complete tour of Menlo Park, ending a period of many months in which newspapermen had been banned. Fox spent several days making notes and sketches. When his story appeared, in the New York *Herald* for Sunday, December 21, 1879, it was the scoop of the decade. The headlines, following the style of the day, were only a single column wide, but they gave the exciting news adequately enough.

Fox wrote lyrically of Edison's filament, a "tiny strip of paper that a breath would blow away." He did his best to explain why it did not burn up and how, when an electric current passed through it, it yielded "a bright, beautiful light, like the mellow sunset of an Italian autumn . . . a light that is like a little globe of sunshine, a veritable Aladdin's lamp." The article caused a sensation. The stock market was closed for the weekend, luckily for the shareholders of the gas companies, but the new light was discussed in tones that varied from fascination to bewilderment to skepticism. The detailed diagrams of the lamps and the dynamo, checked for accuracy by Batchelor and Upton, helped to dispel the notion that Fox's full-page article was merely a clever hoax. Yet there were plenty of doubters, among them Fox's employers.

On the following morning Thomas D. Connery, the managing editor of the *Herald,* rushed into the office of Albert Orr, the city editor who had approved the Fox story.

"How did that stuff get into the paper?" Connery demanded, according to the reminiscences of another *Herald* man of the

EDISON'S LIGHT.

The Great Inventor's Triumph in Electric Illumination.

A SCRAP OF PAPER.

It Makes a Light, Without Gas or Flame, Cheaper Than Oil.

TRANSFORMED IN THE FURNACE.

Complete Details of the Perfected Carbon Lamp.

FIFTEEN MONTHS OF TOIL.

Story of His Tireless Experiments with Lamps, Burners and Generators.

SUCCESS IN A COTTON THREAD.

The Wizard's Byplay, with Bodily Pain and Gold "Tailings."

HISTORY OF ELECTRIC LIGHTING.

—FACSIMILE COPY, *New York Herald,* DECEMBER 21, 1879

time. "Lights strung on wires! You've made a laughing-stock of the *Herald*! What will Bennett * say?"

"He'll probably say that it is the biggest newspaper beat of the times," Orr replied.

"But don't you know that it has been absolutely demonstrated that that kind of light is against the laws of nature? Who wrote the article?"

"Marshall Fox," said Orr, "our star reporter who went with Edison on the eclipse expedition to Wyoming last year."

"How could he allow himself and the paper to be so imposed upon?" Connery shouted. "Where is he? Send for him. We must do something to save ourselves from ridicule. No—don't try to explain—just find Fox and send him to me."

But within a few days neither Fox nor the *Herald* needed to fear ridicule. Edison announced that he was holding open house at Menlo Park every evening through New Year's Eve. The unbelievers were welcome to come and behold the electric light with their own eyes.

Edison was not quite ready, though. What he was creating was the world's first central power station for incandescent lamps, and it took some careful planning. (The first central power station of any kind had gone into service in San Francisco three months earlier—supplying arc light service, however.) The span of six weeks Lowrey had allowed him was not enough to complete the preparations. His decision to open the laboratory the week before New Year's only made things more complicated. Once Fox's December 21 article had been published, daily crowds of visitors flocked uninvited to Menlo Park in advance of New Year's Eve. As the New York *Herald* reported on January 2, 1880:

> To satisfy the curiosity of the earnest inquirers on science, and to practically answer the critics and sceptics, Mr.

* James Gordon Bennett, the publisher of the *Herald*.

Edison ordered the doors of his laboratories thrown wide open, that all might see and judge of his electric light . . . he set no particular night for the public exhibition of the same but directed a week ago that no person who should come to Menlo Park to see the electric light be excluded from the laboratory. Availing themselves of the privilege hundreds of persons came from all quarters. During the first few days the crowds were not too large to interfere with the business of the inventor's assistants, and all went well. Every courtesy was shown and every detail of the new system of lighting explained. The crowds, however, kept increasing. The railroad company ordered extra trains to be run and carriages came streaming from near and far. Surging crowds filed into the laboratory, machine shop and private office of the scientist, and all work had to be practically suspended.

The climax came on December 31. All day long, Edison's shop boys worked to shovel away the snow on the plank walk that led from the railway station to the laboratory; in late afternoon came another light snowfall, so that there was fresh white snow under foot as the fashionable ladies and gentlemen trooped in double file from the trains. There were three thousand sightseers in all that evening. Such celebrities as Henry Ward Beecher, Chauncey M. Depew, General Ben Butler, and Carl Schurz were there. So was the rival inventor, William Sawyer, who appeared intoxicated and roamed through the crowds, bitterly crying that it was all a trick.

They had expected to see infinite wonders, but actually Edison had time to rig only a few dozen lamps. Two light globes framed the gate of the small library-and-office building; eight lamps were strung on wooden poles outside the laboratory; and in the main laboratory a miniature central station kindled thirty lights wired in parallel. It was not much, but it was more than enough to produce a spectacular effect.

"There's Edison!" the visitors cried, and indeed Edison moved

137

among them, smiling, explaining, predicting. He wore his working clothes, and appeared tieless, his vest unbuttoned. Tonight's display, he said, was only a sample of what lay ahead. Soon he would illuminate all of Menlo Park and everything for a square mile around with 800 incandescent lights. Then he would go on to New York, to Newark, to every city in the nation. The lamps would sell for a low price, and would be far less costly to operate than gas jets. The future was his.

The excitement of the crowd mounted as the hours passed. The *Herald* story of January 2 relates how

> the people came by hundreds in every train. They went pellmell through places previously kept sacredly private. Notices not to touch or handle apparatus were disregarded, the assistants were kept on the jump from early till late guarding the scores of delicate instruments with which the laboratory abounds.

Some of the guests entered the dynamo room and were distressed to have their pocket watches magnetized. One elegant coiffure was disarrayed when its owner bent too close to one of the dynamos and found the hairpins leaving her head. A vacuum pump was broken in the crush, and eight of the precious lights were stolen by souvenir hunters.

The general mood was one of awe and admiration, but the disgruntled William Sawyer was not the only malicious visitor. In the throng were representatives of the gas companies, who loudly expressed their disdain for the new light. And there was at least one deliberate vandal, perhaps in the pay of the gas people. He was, Edison later wrote,

> a well-known electrician, graduate of Johns Hopkins University. We had the lamps exhibited in a large room, and so arranged on a table as to illustrate the regular layout of circuits for houses and streets. Sixty of the men employed at the laboratory were used as watchers, each to keep an

138

Edison, standing before a "Z" dynamo of the Edison Electric Light Company.

(above), Winter scene at the Edison Laboratory, Menlo Park, New Jersey.
(below), Electric meter, from a contemporary drawing.

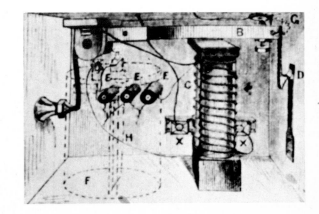

(right), Dynamos in Edison's laboratory at Menlo Park, from a contemporary drawing.
(below), Edison Electric Light Company wagon and coal scale.

Pearl Street, the first Edison Electric Lighting Station in New York. *(above)*, The dynamo room *(below)*, the boiler room from contemporary drawings.

eye on a certain section of the exhibit, and see there was no
monkeying with it. This man had a length of insulated No.
10 wire around his sleeve and back, so that his hands would
conceal the ends, and no one would know he had it. His
idea, of course, was to put this across the ends of the
supplying circuits and short-circuit the whole thing—put it
all out of business without being detected. Then he could
report how easily the electric light went out and a false
impression would be conveyed to the public. He did not
know that we had already worked out the safety fuse, and
that every little group of lights was protected independently.
He slyly put this jumper in contact with the wires—and
just four lamps went out on the section he tampered with.
The watchers saw him do it, however, and got hold of him,
and just led him out of the place with language that made
the recording angels jump to their typewriters.

When the last sightseer had departed, early on the first
morning of the new year, Edison's men gathered around him to
congratulate him. They had prepared a little skit for him—a
parody on the currently popular operetta, *H.M.S. Pinafore*. A
laboratory assistant named MacGregor went to the organ
Edison had installed, struck a few notes, and sang, "I am the
Wizard of the electric light."

The others responded: "And a wide-awake Wizard too!"

MacGregor sang;

"I see you're rather bright and appreciate the might
Of what I daily do.
Quadruplex telegraph or funny phonograph,
It's all the same to me:
With ideas I evolve and problems that I solve
I'm never, never stumped, you see."

The chorus asked: "What, never?"

"No, never!"

"What, never?"

"Well, hardly ever!"

The reactions to the demonstration came in over the next

139

few days. They were highly enthusiastic. One writer described the lamps as

> about four inches long, small and delicate, and comely enough for use in any apartment. They can be removed from a chandelier as readily as a glass stopper from a bottle and by the same motion. The current is turned on and off by the simple means of pressing a button. The lamp is simplicity itself in form and construction, and can be made for a very small sum.

The popular magazine, *Leslie's Weekly*, casually plagiarized Marshall Fox's December 21 article for its own issue of January 10, 1880, rhapsodizing about the "bright, beautiful light, like the mellow sunset of an Italian autumn." Henry Villard, a German-born financier and railroad magnate, provided the most tangible response to what he had seen on New Year's Eve: he ordered an Edison lighting system for his new ship.

Villard was just beginning his brief but astonishing dominance of the railroads of the western United States; he had not yet carried off the overnight market coup by which, a few months later, he would win command of the Northern Pacific Railroad. But he already controlled several smaller companies, among them the Oregon Railway & Navigation Company, which had recently commissioned the *S.S. Columbia*, a 334-foot, 3200-ton steel vessel. The *Columbia* was due to sail from its Pennsylvania shipyard for California, via Cape Horn, in May, 1880. Could Edison complete the lighting job by then, Villard asked?

Edison treated the assignment as the trial run for the future production of "isolated" generating stations. Although he expected to market electricity in cities from central power stations, he also planned to sell isolated stations for use in factories, ships, large homes, and rural districts. For Villard, Edison constructed four of his twin-columned Mary-Ann dynamos and put them in the *Columbia's* engine room, to be driven by a pair of steam engines. A system of belts, shafts, and pulleys linked engines and dynamos, and a multiple circuit was carried through the ship to supply power for 115 lamps with carbonized paper filaments. The work was finished in time for the launching; the *Columbia* made a grand show as it steamed down Delaware Bay by night, all its lights ablaze. There were dire predictions of calamity, based on the tendency of the new arc light systems to go up in flames. But the ship arrived safely in San Francisco after a two-month voyage, during which its electric lamps had given 415 hours of continuous service without the failure of a single bulb. This impressive feat lead *Herald* publisher James Gordon Bennett to install an Edison isolated system on his yacht, and soon afterward Jay Gould, who destested Bennett, ordered an even larger Edison plant for *his* yacht.

The lighting business was off to a good start, but Edison saw room for improvement, both in his dynamo and particularly in his lamp filament. The paper filament was too difficult to make, and the basic material was unreliable; invisible defects in the paper caused too many lamps to fail. Edison had another motive for wishing to abandon the use of carbonized paper. Swan had patented a paper filament lamp in England and Sawyer had patented one in the United States. Infringement suits were inevitable. Edison thought he might win in court, but he had learned the advisability of avoiding litigation wherever possible. With some totally new kind of filament he could sidestep any such obstacles.

So the search that had halted at the end of October now resumed. Edison and his men carbonized everything they could get their hands on, including leather, macaroni, pomegranate peel, onion rind, and hundreds of types of wood. Even the umbrellas and walking-sticks of unwary guests were tapped for samples. Edison's romantic early biographers would have us believe that the ultimate discovery, when it came, was again made by chance, and perhaps this time it was. As one of them tells it, Edison casually picked up a palm-leaf fan while discussing some aspect of his work. "As he spoke, he ran his sensitive fingers around the rim of the fan. It was made of bamboo, a strip cut from the outer surface of the tree. Suddenly, he stopped fingering the fan-rim, and examined it closely.

" 'Batch,' he called, rising abruptly, 'take this bamboo strip, cut it up, and get out of it all the filaments you can!' "

Perhaps so. In any event, the bamboo strip produced the best filament material thus far. Its strong fibers, arranged in parallel rows, were ideal for an incandescent lamp.

There were, Edison learned, thousands of species of bamboo. Which one was best suited for the filament? Partly out of scientific zeal, and partly out of sheer love of publicity, Edison now conceived a fantastic quest worthy of the imagination of Jules Verne. He proposed to send scouts into the most remote jungles of the world to find the perfect bamboo.

It would be an expensive amusement, but he had plenty of cash at his disposal. The success of the New Year's Eve demonstration had loosened the purse-strings of the Edison Electric Light investors. At the beginning of the year they had turned over to Edison $57,568 for future developmental expenses, more than he had spent all through 1879; that money went for drab things such as dynamos, copper wire, and steam engines. A few months later he went to them for another liberal transfusion of cash, this time to finance his bamboo hunt. They gave it to him. With their $100 shares of Edison Electric Light stock now worth upwards of three thousand dollars apiece, they had reason to see that Edison's public-relations pranks had cash value. All told they would advance Edison more than one hundred and fifty thousand dollars in 1880.

With appropriate fanfare the explorers departed. The first to leave, in the summer of 1880, was William H. Moore of New Jersey. His destination was Japan and China. A man named

142

Segredor was dispatched to the West Indies and Central America, but died of yellow fever in Cuba. John C. Brauner left for the Brazilian port of Pará, and fought his way two thousand miles up the Amazon to snip bamboo samples in swamps and rain forests. The goal of C. F. Hanington was the valley of the Rio de la Plata, so that he could ransack Argentina, Paraguay, and Uruguay.

A mining prospector named Frank McGowan entered the wilds of Colombia, Ecuador, and Peru. He went ninety-eight days without removing his clothes, fought off deadly snakes and hostile natives, contracted tropical fevers, and was deserted by his guides. Somehow he got back to Menlo Park after fifteen months, delivered his bamboo samples, and was rewarded by Edison with a generous cash bonus. McGowan gathered his friends for a lavish dinner at a New York cafe, where he discoursed to great effect on his picturesque adventures and extraordinary sufferings. He bade his friends good night at the door of the restaurant, walked off in the direction of the West Side docks, and was never seen again—a mystery that titillated newspaper readers for several years.

Another dauntless traveler was James Ricalton, a New Jersey schoolmaster. Edison presented him with a bamboo specimen of unknown origin that some explorer had sent him from Asia, and ordered Ricalton to find its source. Ricalton sailed for the Orient by way of the Suez Canal and covered thirty thousand miles through Ceylon, India, Burma, the Malay Peninsula, China, and Japan. He was home twelve months to the day after his departure, and Edison, shouldering through the crowd of reporters at the pier, demanded, "Did you *get* it?" But Ricalton had not.

In all, six thousand species of bamboo reached Menlo Park, each to be peeled, carbonized, and tested. Edison received a gratifying amount of space in the journals of the day, and incidentally consumed a remarkable quantity of the money of Vanderbilt, Morgan, and his other backers. But most of the travail had been needless. Edison's first emissary, William Moore, had known a good deal about the bamboo trade. Moore had gone straight to a dealer in Japan and had obtained a reliable supply of excellent bamboo at a reasonable cost. Moore's samples reached Menlo Park even before some of the other heroes had set out, and nothing better was discovered in all the subsequent adventuring. Between 1880 and 1889, when bamboo filament lamps became obsolete, a single plantation in Japan supplied Edison's needs. A few wagonloads of bamboo each year sufficed to fashion the millions of filaments in the Edison lamps that were lighting the world.

nine

A Busy Year at Menlo Park

EDISON'S competitors and detractors were not idle during 1880. On every side, rival schemes for electric illumination were proceeding rapidly.

Some were ludicrous, like the system first announced in the *Scientific American* for June 21, 1879, under the heading, "Practical Divisibility of the Electric Light." This was nothing less than an idea for lighting the interior of homes by placing enormous arc lights on staircases and deflecting the beam through mirrors and wall openings into the rooms. Two civil engineers named Molera and Cebrian, of San Francisco, were the authors of this project. Their prospectus declared,

> There are certain practical difficulties in dividing the electrical current, so as to produce a number of small lights by means of a single generator, which have baffled the ingenuity of inventors so far, and which must effectually block the progress of subdivision in this direction, unless some new principle is discovered. It is stated that no matter how cheap the original current may be produced, the loss by division is so great that small lights must be expensive.

The Molera-Cebrian system, employing "optical contrivances,

leaving the current undisturbed and undivided, doing away with expensive electrical conductors, and dispensing with lamps or regulators at points where the lighting is to be utilized," seemed highly promising until Edison's demonstrations at the end of the year showed its absurdity. But the idea was not put to rest until well into 1880.

Joseph Swan was mounting a more serious challenge in England. In the early and unworldly days of his research, Swan had not bothered with patents, and soon he found himself hedged about in his own country by five Edison patents. Most of these covered the platinum filament and carbonized thread filament lamps. Swan speedily learned Edison's technique and filed a cluster of patent applications himself as fast as he could produce improvements in the incandescent lamp. In 1880 he took out a patent on the process of removing occluded gases from the filament before sealing the lamp. He and Edison had arrived at the same principle independently, using the Sprengel pump, but Swan moved faster to get the English patent. That left Edison at a serious disadvantage in England. Late in 1880 Swan had his own manufacturing company and began to take orders for incandescent lighting systems.

The arc light people were also active. One of the arc light's most enthusiastic exponents was Professor Elihu Thomson of Philadelphia, the brilliant young electrical engineer who, with Edwin J. Houston, had conducted the Franklin Institute's dynamo tests in 1878. Thomson and Houston had since formed their own partnership and had taken out several patents for dynamo design. The Thomson-Houston system permitted individual lamps to be switched on and off at will without upsetting the circuit, an important improvement in arc light theory.

In January of 1880 Thomson visited Menlo Park to observe Edison's progress. With the curious courtesy that rival inventors extended to one another then, Edison gave him the full tour and even presented Thomson with an incandescent lamp. Despite this cordiality, Thomson upon his return to Philadelphia declared that he "did not think very highly of the Edison lamp and expected no great future for it." The light was too dim, he said, and he did not see how Edison could possibly afford to set up his intended system of parallel circuitry, with conducting mains and branch wires carrying power into a multitude of homes. It would, said Thomson, require "all the copper in the world." This gloomy prediction reached the directors of Edison Electric Light and effectively undid the optimism that had been kindled on New Year's Eve. They began to worry again about Edison's scheme.

A few months later Thomson and Houston were in direct competition with Edison. A group of New England investors put up capital to form the American Electric Company, which acquired the Thomson-Houston patents. The two professors moved to New Britain, Connecticut, and began to design new dynamos for commercial installation. Out of this small, not very successful company would grow the great Thomson-Houston Electric Company that was to bedevil Edison for nearly a decade and ultimately engulf his own electrical enterprise.

The Brush Electric Company of Cleveland, the pioneer in American arc light systems, was making great strides in 1880. Brush moved from triumph to triumph: John Wanamaker's store in Philadelphia, Cleveland's streets, San Francisco, Niagara Falls, and Wabash, Indiana. By the summer of 1880 isolated Brush plants lit a number of factories and hotels in several cities; in Philadelphia, the Continental Hotel on Chestnut Street replaced 144 gas burners in its dining room with two large Brush lamps, running a dynamo from the steam engine of the hotel elevator.

Brush shortly organized a subsidiary, Brush Electric Light Company of New York, which in September of 1880 completed a pilot plant on West 25th Street. Obtaining permission to install its lights on Broadway, Brush ran an experimental line

147

of arc lights for three quarters of a mile along Broadway in mid-December. The initial night of service was less than successful, as a newspaper account of December 19, 1880 makes clear:

> A large number of people were attracted to the vicinity of the Fifth Avenue Hotel last night by the announcement that the first experiment of lighting Broadway by electricity would be made near that point during the evening. From Fourteenth Street up to Thirty-fourth Street at every corner was a tall iron post upon which had been placed one of the lamps, and each one from dark till about ten o'clock was intently watched by a little knot of patient waiters. After that time the street resumed its usual appearance, the crowd gradually thinning out in deep disappointment. At a quarter before twelve the current was turned on to test the circuit, and for a few moments Broadway from Fourteenth Street to Twenty-sixth Street, as far as the lamps have been connected, was vividly bright, but soon grew darker and darker as the lights flickered, one by one, and went out. Some kept up a spasmodic blaze for twenty minutes when the current was turned off and the gas was left in undisputed possession. The failure of the trial is explained by the managers to be due to the improper adjustment of the attachments, most of the lamps having been put up after dark. On Monday night at six o'clock all the lights will be in running order, when the illumination, which is to last all night, will take place.

Despite this mishap the Brush lights soon were a familiar part of the Broadway environment. Brush Electric Light received a contract from the city fathers to illuminate Union and Madison Squares with arc lights mounted on masts 160 feet high. There were also orders from private customers: the Brunswick and Sturtevant Hotels, the Park Theater, and Koster and Bial's music hall.

Philadelphia, where arc lights by now were no novelties, organized a Brush Electric Light Company of its own in March of 1881. Local investors put up $200,000 to license the rights to use Brush equipment and incorporated "for the purpose of carrying on the business of manufacturing, procuring, owning and operating various apparatus used in producing light, heat, or power by electricity or used in lighting buildings." Brush Electric of Philadelphia chose as its first project the lighting of Chestnut street at its own expense; after a one-year trial, the city government could decide if it wished to offer a permanent contract.

Following the pattern set down in San Francisco in 1879, the Philadelphia company built a central power station just north of Chestnut between 20th and 21st Streets. It was equipped with eight dynamos and eight steam engines. Iron poles 40 feet high, painted bright red, began to rise along Chestnut Street, and from them were stretched the high-voltage power lines and the Brush arc lamps. The project was not unanimously admired. One citizen wrote to the *Public Ledger,* a newspaper of the day:

> No resident west of Broad Street desires the electric light. Would any one of the editors or owners of the daily papers like one in front of his private dwelling? Would Mayor King or any member of Councils be delighted with one in front of his sleeping chamber? There is no city in the world where it would be tolerated in a street occupied almost entirely by private residences as West Chestnut Street is. Do you admire the six red poles in each square?

All the same, forty-nine Chestnut Street lights were turned on on December 3, 1881. A newspaper reported, "With the combined efforts of the moonlight, electric light, and gaslight, Chestnut Street was better lit upon Saturday and Sunday nights than at any time in its history."

The arc light was taking firm possession of America's great cities. The backers of Edison Electric Light waited restlessly for signs of progress. The gas companies, annoyed but not mortally wounded by the spread of arc lights in the streets, grew more confident that Edison's indoor system would never materialize

149

as a commercial competitor. Cyprien Marie Tessie du Motay, a French-born inventor and chemist who had developed the most successful method for the manufacture of gas, spoke scornfully of Edison's work as "new electric playthings . . . the experiments of a semi-practical prestidigitateur. . . . something very amusing, perhaps." However, the six gas companies of New York City, anticipating future difficulties with Edison, negotiated a peace treaty among themselves on March 30, 1880. The rate war came to an end, service districts were clearly assigned to avoid ruinous competition, and there was talk of an ultimate merger into one powerful company that would sell gas to all of New York.

Edison, toiling at Menlo Park, kept his own counsel.

The excitement over finding a successful incandescent lamp had subsided early in the new year. He had turned to the much more difficult problem of creating a system of electrical distribution. Edison's original plan, which he had employed for his New Year's Eve demonstration, had made use of the so-called "tree" circuit: a pair of large conducting mains coming from the dynamo and branching into ever-smaller lines that carried current to the individual lamps. But, as Elihu Thomson had correctly predicted, such a system would devour an inordinate amount of copper; the main conductors would have to equal in size the entire remaining structure of branch conductors. For an 8,000-lamp circuit covering nine city blocks, Edison discovered, he would need about eight hundred thousand pounds of copper at a cost of $200,000. To light all of New York City would cost billions.

With remarkable speed Edison worked out a more economical transmission system. On January 28, 1880, he applied for a patent on his "System of Electrical Distribution," providing for multiple-arc distribution of current from a number of generators. This patent—which was not granted until August 30, 1887—was the basis of the Edison power system.

The system was not yet complete, but this basic patent gave Edison the foundation for further improvement. As a trade journal of the time, the *Electrical Review*, commented,

> It would seem as if the entire field of multiple distribution were now in the hands of the owners of this patent—about as broad as a patent can be, being regardless of specific devices, and laying a powerful grasp on the fundamental idea of multiple distribution from a number of generators throughout a metallic circuit.

The improvements came steadily. (Edison took out 60 patents in all during 1880—7 on transmission systems, 6 on dynamos, 32 on incandescent lamp refinements, and many on auxiliary parts.) The great breakthrough was made in the summer of that year with the discovery of the "feeder and main" concept. This system not only allowed a sharp reduction in the amount of copper needed, but avoided another distribution problem, the drop in voltage over distance that tended to make outlying lights dimmer than those near the generating station. No longer did Edison connect his huge conducting mains directly to the dynamos. Instead, smaller lines called "feeders" carried power to short sections of main located at points of heavy lamp concentration. The drop in voltage took place only in the feeder; say, from 120 volts to 110. But the 110-volt current remained constant as it traveled the short distance from the local main to the local distributing circuits. With a system of feeders and mains, the copper cost for Edison's pilot nine-block 8,000-lamp circuit dropped from $200,000 to $30,000. When the system was demonstrated in England, the great physicist, Lord Kelvin, was asked why no one had ever thought of anything so simple before. He replied, "The only answer I can think of is that no one else is Edison."

By way of relaxation during this work, Edison amused himself by constructing an electric railway at Menlo Park. It was not the first of its type; as early as 1835, a Vermont inventor had operated a miniature railway with a battery-powered engine, and in 1839 a 5-ton electric locomotive had been driven between Glasgow and Edinburgh. Dr. E. Werner von Siemens of Germany had built an electric railway in Berlin in 1879 that drew current from a dynamo, not from batteries.

Edison's railway had a narrow-gauge track about a third of a mile long, running in a circular path around a hill near the laboratory. For a locomotive he took a four-wheeled truck and laid one of his Long-waisted Mary Ann dynamos sidewise on it to function as a motor—for it was already recognized that a dynamo running in reverse would serve as an electric motor, converting electrical energy back into mechanical energy. The power for the locomotive came from the generating station behind the laboratory that was normally used for the light circuit. A pair of dynamos there generated 75 amperes of current at 110 volts, and this was carried by wires to the metal track. The metal rims of the locomotive wheels drew the current from the rails to the motor, and an awkward arrangement of pulleys and wheels transmitted the power via the motor to the driving axle.

Edison's love of trains, of course, went back to his Port Huron boyhood, and he took great pleasure in watching John Kruesi put the locomotive together in the machine shop. At Edison's insistence a great searchlight was added to the head of the locomotive, and a bell to warn off cows was mounted on it also. An open-cabin passenger car was coupled behind.

The first trial of the train came on May 13, 1880. Newspapermen and townsfolk were present in large numbers as Edison clambered aboard the locomotive. Charles Batchelor sat beside him with his gifted hands on the throttle. There were some twenty passengers. "All aboard!" Edison cried, and Batchelor closed the switch. The little train jogged pleasantly down the track at a speed of twenty miles an hour. But when Batchelor tried to bring it to a halt, the driving wheels gave way and the locomotive was disabled. "We walked back pushing the train with us," recalled Francis Jehl, one of the passengers.

It had begun more or less as a toy, but Edison found himself taking it more seriously almost at once. The locomotive was repaired and the track extended, and in three weeks of intensive trials Edison got the train up to forty miles an hour without mishap. Early in June he decided to exhibit it for his financial backers of the Edison Electric Light Company. Grosvenor Lowrey somewhat reluctantly went along for the ride, and was grumbling about the high speed when the train jumped the track. Kruesi, who was at the controls, was thrown off and landed on his face; another man was pitched in a somersault through some underbrush. Lowrey wrote to his wife,

> Edison was off in a minute, jumping and laughing, and declaring it was a "daisy." Kruesi got up, his face bleeding and a good deal shaken; and I shall never forget the expression of voice in which he said, with some foreign accent: "Oh! Yes, pairfeckly safe!" Fortunately no other hurts were suffered, and in a few minutes we had the train on the track again.

Henry Villard, now the head of the Northern Pacific Railroad and suddenly one of America's most potent financiers, had recently joined the board of directors of Edison Electric Light. He saw a great future for the electric railway, and when his conservative fellow-directors refused to get involved with the thing, Villard himself advanced Edison $40,000 for further development. This was in the summer of 1881. Both Villard and Edison apparently had in mind long-haul freight service, and not the local intra-city service for which electric trains would eventually be used. They organized the Electric Railway Company of America in 1883, but by then Edison had withdrawn from personal participation in this side venture. "I could not go on with it," he told an interviewer in the summer of 1884. "I had too many other things to attend to, especially in connection with electric lighting."

To the relief of his backers, Edison was again concentrating on the business at hand soon after the bumpy train ride of June, 1880. With the feeder-and-main problem behind him, he felt almost ready to get his system into commercial use.

Almost. He wanted it to be perfect before he started looking for lighting customers, but perfection was a difficult goal. Edison Electric Light stock gyrated wildly as Edison neared the end of his preliminary work, then in a fit of dissatisfaction scrapped everything and took a different approach. He was harsh in his self-criticism. He kept discovering new ways to improve his dynamos and his transmission system; each improvement set the work back by a month or two, while the arc light companies continued their inexorable invasion of the cities.

The backers were demanding an end to the research. They wanted Edison to install a large-scale lighting system at Menlo Park, so that they could judge its efficiency and operating cost before advancing any more money. His laboratory was becoming a bottomless sink for dollars. Sensing their impatience, Edison agreed to stage a second end-of-the-year demonstration of his system at Menlo Park.

The 1879 show, for all its impact, had really proved nothing more than that Edison had a workable incandescent lamp. This year he would have to show that he was ready with a total system of generating, transmitting, and distributing power. He blocked out an area in Menlo Park half a mile square around the laboratory and set up white wooden lampposts where street corners would have been, if the town had had any streets. His plan called for wiring the houses within this area—all half-dozen of them—plus his own laboratory buildings and shops. In late summer Edison's workmen began to dig trenches for the underground conduits and conducting mains—eight miles of

154

wiring, altogether, to reach four hundred and twenty-five 16-candlepower lamps.

The underground distribution system was an essential part of Edison's idea. In 1880 the streets of America's cities were hideously disfigured by overhead power lines, and the ugly array was growing worse month by month as telephone wires and arc light lines joined the telegraph lines already present. Although it was costlier to put power lines underground—and might not even be technically possible—Edison had early resolved that his lights would add nothing to the overhead blight.

The chief problem of underground distribution was insulation. The experts agreed that the current would surely bleed away uselessly into the earth. Since no one had ever laid power lines in the ground before, Edison, in the summer of 1880, had to conceive the technology of insulation from scratch.

He felt at first that by using low voltages he would avoid the insulation problem entirely, so his first lines consisted of nothing more than bare copper wire encased in wooden molding. But it quickly turned out that there were high power losses even at 110 volts. The leakage of electricity blew out the whole circuit. Experiments to find an effective insulating material began at once. Edison's chemists tried coal tar, powdered slate, and muslin wrappings, without success. Then Wilson S. Howell of the Edison staff suggested a mixture of asphalt and oxidized linseed oil blended with paraffin and beeswax. Amid a foul odor he cooked up a batch of the stuff; it passed the tests. Farm boys were hired to wind muslin strips soaked in Howell's fragrant compound around the lengths of copper wire.

By the beginning of November, 1880, the lines were in the ground and the trenches had been filled. A central power station in one of the laboratory buildings held eleven of the "Z-type" dynamos, as the Long-waisted Mary Anns now were called. Edison was far from pleased with this elaborate assemblage of small dynamos, which were connected by an intricate

155

and inefficient system of belts to the steam engines that drove them. With the deadline for his December demonstration fast approaching, he began to draw plans for a large-capacity dynamo that would be directly linked, without belts, to a large steam engine.

Such a direct-coupled machine was unknown then. All existing dynamos had belt attachments connecting them to relatively slow-moving steam engines that operated at 66 to 100 revolutions per minute. Edison envisioned a single generating unit mounted on the same iron bedplate, with a steam engine turning at hundreds of revolutions a minute and producing a high power output.

He called in Charles T. Porter, whose firm manufactured the highly regarded Porter-Allen steam engines, and described his requirements. As he told the story later, Edison said to Porter, " 'I want a 150-horsepower engine to run 700 revolutions a minute.' He hummed and hawed a bit and then agreed to build it—if I could pay for it! I believe he charged me $4200 for it." Edison asked for delivery by Christmas, so he could use the big Porter-Allen engine in his New Year's Eve demonstration. Porter agreed to do his best, but doubted that he could manage to assemble the machine so quickly.

The first test of Edison's Menlo Park system came on Election Day, 1880. Edison was a firm supporter of the Republican Presidential candidate, James A. Garfield. "If Garfield is elected," he said, "light the circuit." The returns came clicking in over Edison's plant telegraph all day, and by dusk Garfield's slim lead over Democrat Winfield S. Hancock was incontestable. The lights of Menlo Park glowed that night.

Edison's mood was far from gay, though, and as the days shortened he grew tense and uneasy. It was now certain that his Porter-Allen steam engine was going to arrive too late for his demonstration. The Babcock-Wilcox boilers he had ordered to provide the engine with steam would also be late. His system still looked tentative to him, a patched-together improvisation. A reporter who interviewed him in December found him "sunk in melancholy," an uncharacteristic pose for Edison. The imperfections of his electrical system were not his only problems. Hiram Maxim, a rival inventor, had gone into the business of making incandescent lamps and was hiring away some of Edison's best men at high salaries. Among those who went over to Maxim was Ludwig Boehm, the gifted German glass blower who had produced Edison's experimental bulbs. Soon Maxim was marketing incandescent lights similar in all essential respects to Edison's, forcing Edison, who hated patent litigation, to consider suing. In England, Swan was also producing incandescent lights much like Edison's. So tangled was the English patent situation that it was difficult to say if Swan were infringing on Edison or Edison on Swan. Another dreary lawsuit seemed inevitable.

However gloomy Edison was just then, his backers were buoyed by the prospect of at last getting some return on their investment. Grosvenor Lowrey was making preliminary inquiries in New York City about obtaining a municipal franchise to sell incandescent lighting. An odd legal problem appeared at once. As the 1881 annual report to the stockholders of the Edison Electric Light Company explained it:

> Originally your board intended to have this company itself light up an initial or model station in this city. That plan was changed because it was found that under the laws of the state the use of the streets could be obtained only by a company organized under the Gas Statutes. Consequently a new company, known as the Edison Electric Illuminating Company of New York, was formed to install the first model station.

That is, the charter of Edison Electric Light was worded in such a way to prevent the company from digging up the streets

157

of New York to lay conducting mains. The new corporation, with a charter that conformed to the regulations, was organized on December 16, 1880 as a subsidiary of the parent company. Thus Edison Electric Illuminating Company of New York—the earliest ancestor of today's vast Consolidated Edison Company—came into being to serve as an operating entity. Edison Electric Light would remain simply a patent-holding corporation that would license its rights to Edison Illuminating and any subsequent local utilities that might be organized.

This dual arrangement ultimately caused Edison a great deal of grief. His patent rights were vested in a holding company that could license subsidiaries as it pleased, without itself taking any of the risks involved in selling power to the public. Originally he had owned 2500 of that parent company's 3000 shares. But he had sold some of his stock to raise funds for research, and new shares had been issued to others as the need for additional capital arose. By the end of 1880 he held only a minority position in the stock of Edison Electric Light; the lion's share of control had passed to J. P. Morgan and his associates. From that time on, Edison would find himself in a continuing struggle with Morgan for the use of his own patents.

Some hint of the coming trouble is shown by the list of officers and directors chosen by the new Edison Illuminating at its first official meeting on December 20, 1880. The president elected was Norvin Green of Western Union, Eggisto Fabbri of Morgan's banking firm was named treasurer, and Calvin Goddard of Western Union became secretary. The board of directors consisted of a group of influential stockholders in Edison Electric Light: Tracy Edson, Robert Cutting, Nathan Miller, James Banker, Grosvenor Lowrey, S. B. Eaton, Robert Galloway, James Green, and Fabbri. Edison's name is not to be found on either list. Not until December 16, 1881, does he show up in the records of Edison Illuminating, and then merely with the title of "engineer." Soon after, he was added to the board of directors, but his voice in the running of the company was never a strong one. The inventor's invention had begun to get away from him.

The officers of the new corporation lost no time applying for a New York franchise. Four days after the incorporation of Edison Illuminating, the New York City Board of Aldermen came out en masse to Menlo Park to take a look at the new lights.

Tammany Hall was then in full domination of the metropolis. Although the infamous Boss Tweed had been overthrown a decade earlier, corruption was still the order of the day in municipal government, and New York's aldermen were a dull-witted, venal bunch of political hacks, for sale to the highest bidder. When they appeared, late on the afternoon of December 20, 1880, Edison was hard put to conceal his distaste for them. Nervously Edison greeted the legislators and offered a curt one-sentence speech of welcome.

An account of the visit in a newspaper called *Truth* declared that Edison was

> the most unpretending person present. He was dressed in his usual careless style and looked as blandly innocent as usual. Entertainment included a demonstration of the lighting system, the phonograph and loud speaking telephone, a visit to the Edison Library where there was a very complete collection of scientific works which the Tammany men must have found edifying, and an inspection of the map of the Pearl Street district, said to comprise 51 city blocks.*

The display of wonders bored the indifferent politicians. They had been treated well by the worried gas companies, and would remain hostile to Edison unless he offered a higher bid for their loyalty. Grosvenor Lowrey, wise in the ways of handling aldermen, had planned some further entertainment designed to soften their hearts a little. According to *Truth:*

> The City Fathers had begun to look quite dry and hungry and as though refreshments would have looked much more

* This was the district in which Edison proposed to inaugurate his New York City lighting service.

159

palatable to them than the display of inventions they had
been wondering at for two hours without a great deal of
comprehension although with a wonderful exhibition of
understanding and appreciation. Their hopes were quickly
realized by the announcement that the collation, served by
Delmonico, was ready. For half an hour only the clatter
of dishes and the popping of champagne corks could be
heard and then the wine began to work and the Aldermen,
true to their political instincts, began to howl, "Speech,
Speech." One of the witnesses of this visit said that the
City Fathers were amazed at the appearance of the man
they called "Professor" Edison. "Why," whispered one City
Father to another, "he looks like a regular fellow. See how
he handles his cigar—just like the boys in the Wigwam
[Tammany Hall]."

The champagne and cigars mellowed the legislators; they
offered toast after toast to Edison, who was embarrassed and ill
at ease at their attentions. But they left without making any
commitment to give Edison Illuminating a city franchise. They
seemed too deeply enmeshed with the gas company lobbyists,
and progress for progress' sake did not delight them. One alder-
man was heard to point out that Edison's light would take away
the jobs of hundreds of lamplighters; another observed that the
lamplighters were voters, but the new machines did not cast a
single vote. It was suggested that Edison might get his franchise
—for a tax, say, of $1000 per mile of conduit. "All in all," a
newspaper observed, "Mr. Edison's tests were a decided success,
especially of his guests' capacity for champaigne." The New
York *Express* noted in headline form a few days later: "City
Fathers dozing—a dull session of the Common Council in the
City Hall today regaling themselves over reminiscenses of a
pilgrimage to Menlo Park."

It was a snowy Christmas. The promised public demonstration now took place, and, night after night, the public descended
on Menlo Park as it had done exactly twelve months earlier. The

year's progress was impressive. Where in 1879 there had been just a few dozen lamps and a single small dynamo, now Edison had a complete central station in operation, supplying hundreds of lights. Although he grieved at the absence of his Porter-Allen steam engine, he still put on a splendid show. The New York *Herald* described the event in its edition for January 2, 1880:

> In every direction stretched out long lines of electric lights, whose lustre made wide white circles on the white-clad earth. One could not tire of gazing at those starry lines. Edison did not bother about his overcoat as he walked in the open air. In an instant all was dark . . . in another instant the whole scene of fire and ice sprang into being again. "Eight miles of wire!" Edison exclaimed; and yet he observed, some people were not satisfied with his demonstration.

The backers were worrying, the politicians were uncooperative, the system had not yet really proved itself. 1880 faded into memory as 1879 had done: with the outcome of the great enterprise still in doubt.

ten

Pearl
Street

EARLY in 1881 the big Porter-Allen steam engine reached Menlo Park at last. Edison was ready for it. He had designed an enlarged dynamo with huge magnets, and he had it mounted with the steam engine to form a single self-contained generating unit. The new engine was given its first trial one January evening. This is Edison's account:

> We set the machine up in the old shop, and we had some idea of what might happen. So we tied a chain around the throttle valve and ran it out through a window into the wood shed, where we stood to work it. Now the old shop stood on one of those New Jersey shale hills, and every time we opened up the engine and she got to about 300 revolutions the whole hill shook under her. We shut her off and rebalanced and tried again, and after a good deal of trouble we finally did run up to 700, but you should have seen her run! Why, every time the connecting rod went up she tried to lift that whole hill with her! After we got through with this business we tamed her down to 350 revolutions (which was all I wanted), and then everybody said, "Why, how beautifully it runs, and how practicable such an engine is!" We closed a bill for six engines. . . .

Now Edison could begin to think seriously about supplying New York City with electricity. He had already chosen what he designated as his "First District." It covered about a sixth of a square mile of downtown Manhattan, bounded by Wall, Spruce, Ferry, and Nassau Streets, and the East River. The district boundaries were selected with great shrewdness. Edison's First District included a small residential area and a small factory area, thus providing the balance of a daytime power load against a nighttime lighting load that he knew to be the key to economical operation. Even more important, the First District included the financial capital of the nation, the Stock Exchange and the great banking houses, as well as the offices of some of the city's most influential newspapers. When the lights went on in the First District, the bankers, brokers, and editors would be the first to sing their praises.

Edison attacked the task of lighting the First District by studying its current gas consumption. Years later he related,

> I got an insurance map of New York in which every elevator shaft and boiler and house-top and fire-wall was set down, and studied it carefully. Then I laid out a district and figured out an idea of the central station to feed that part of the town. . . . I worked on a system, and soon knew where every hatchway and bulkhead door in the district I had marked was and what every man paid for his gas. How did I know? Simplest thing in the world. I hired a man to start in every day about two o'clock and walk around through the district noting the number of gas lights burning in the various premises; then at three o'clock he went around again and made more notes, and at four o'clock and up to every other hour to two or three o'clock in the morning. In that way it was easy enough to figure out the gas consumption of every tenant and of the whole district.

On January 28, 1881, Edison called in the directors of Edison Electric Light and showed them his complete Menlo Park lighting system in operation, with 425 lamps powered by his big combination dynamo and steam engine. He ran a twelve-hour operating test and produced a set of figures that pleased the financiers far more than the sight of glowing lamps. A ton and a half of coal had been needed to run the 425 lights for twelve hours. That worked out to 0.4 pound of coal per lamp per hour. Edison, armed with his statistics on gas consumption and cost in the First District, was able to prove that he could offer his light at a competitive price. The backers were delighted.

He was ready now to leave Menlo Park and supervise the installation of the lighting plant in New York. "My work here is done, my light is perfected," he told the New York *Herald.* "I'm now going into the *practical production of it.*"

There was still the minor matter of obtaining an operating franchise. The Mayor of New York, an enthusiastic partisan of the gas interests, had gone on record opposing the Edison operation, but a combination of Grosvenor Lowrey's guile and J. P. Morgan's money carried the day. There are no written records of the process whereby the Board of Aldermen was swayed; in the end the legislators agreed to give Edison Illuminating its franchise over the Mayor's objections. On April 19, 1881, the company was officially granted the use of the city streets over a full square mile of lower Manhattan, with no conduit tax to pay.

By then Edison had been living in New York City for two months, and was hard at work on his power station.

Edison's task was complicated by his increasingly difficult relations with his backers. Edison Electric Light owned his patents, and had licensed them to Edison Illuminating in return for a controlling interest in the younger company's stock, but Edison Electric Light did not care to manufacture any of the equipment needed to translate theory into reality. Manufacturing meant putting up capital, and the Morgan group did not propose to risk any capital setting up machine shops and factories. It had made its investment of some five hundred thousand dollars in Edison's research; it did not care to risk very much more than that. Now Edison Electric Light resolved to sit tight, clutching its priceless patents to its bosom, and allow others to run the capital risks.

The impasse had begun to develop as early as the summer of 1880. Edison had asked Edison Electric Light for "millions" to manufacture lamps, fixtures, sockets, switches, dynamos, conductors, and all the other apparatus needed for a city lighting system. Edison Electric Light said no. It would rather let the whole enterprise founder right there than get entangled in the business of manufacturing electrical equipment.

Edison suspected it was a bluff—for the investors would lose all the capital they had already risked if no lighting company materialized—but he saw no way of prodding them to give in. Nor could he find any reliable manufacturing company that would produce what he needed to order. During a patent suit in 1890 he said,

> Wall Street could not see its way clear to finance a new and untried business. We were confronted by a stupendous obstacle. Nowhere in the world could we obtain any of the items or devices necessary for the exploitation of the system. The directors of the Edison Electric Light Company would not go into manufacturing. Thus forced to the wall, I was forced to go into the manufacturing business myself.

He had happily divorced himself from manufacturing in 1876 to found his research laboratory at Menlo Park, and he had no wish to get back into it. But, as he told a financier who declined to back him, "If there are no factories to make my inventions, I will build the factories myself. Since capital is timid, I will raise and supply it. . . . The issue is factories or death!"

Neither Villard nor any of the members of the Morgan group cared even to make a private investment. Edison had to put up over 90 per cent of the capital for the manufacturing companies himself, with Batchelor and a few of his other associates supplying the rest. He borrowed heavily to raise the money, and when he had borrowed all he could, he raised the rest by selling some more of his shares in Edison Electric Light. Thus he continued to surrender slices of what had originally been a controlling interest in the company.

The first of the new companies was the Edison Lamp Company, founded in the summer of 1880 on a capital of $10,000 supplied by Edison, Batchelor, Upton, and Edward Johnson. Its factory was a rickety wooden building across the railway tracks from the Menlo Park laboratory. Edison Electric Light agreed to purchase bulbs from Edison Lamp at a flat rate of 40 cents apiece.

At the outset, Edison had no way of predicting what it would cost him to manufacture the bulbs in quantity. It had been a slow, tortuous process to turn them out in the laboratory, but he counted on developing mass-production techniques. With the help of the Corning Glass Works of Corning, New York, Edison developed a method for blowing the glass bulbs with little breakage, but the real difficulty stemmed from getting the intricate filament and electrical conductor into the bulb, evacuating it, and sealing it. At first more than two hundred operations, all performed by hand, were required for this. Edison discovered that in the Edison Lamp Company's first year of operation the bulbs it was selling to Edison Electric Light for 40 cents apiece cost $1.10 apiece to make.

But he was bound by his contract, and the only way he could keep from being devoured by losses was to lower his production costs through improved efficiency. In 1881 Edison Lamp succeeded in getting its average expense per bulb down to 70 cents; a year later it was 50 cents; and by 1883 it cost only 37 cents to manufacture each bulb. Edison Lamp sold enough bulbs at this 3-cent profit during the year to wipe out the losses of previous years. Eventually the company was producing bulbs at a cost of 22 cents each, which allowed it a fine profit on its resale contract.

A second company turned out the switches, fuses, light fixtures, sockets, and other small appliances. This was Bergmann & Co., headed by Sigmund Bergmann, a veteran of Edison's original Newark factory. For several years Bergmann had run a small machine shop in New York City where he turned out such things as phonographs under contract to Edison. Now, with financial backing from Edison and Edward Johnson, Bergmann opened a new factory on Wooster Street. Within a year he had to expand his quarters and was employing three hundred men.

Producing dynamos and other heavy equipment was the province of a company called the Edison Machine Works, at 104 Goerck Street in downtown Manhattan. The Electric Tube Company on nearby Washington Street manufactured the underground mains and conductors under the supervision of John Kruesi.

In founding these new firms, Edison had the assistance of a young, ambitious Londoner named Samuel Insull, who many years later was to create a giant power-company empire of his own and see it carried to a spectacular collapse in 1929. Insull was a self-made man who had risen from a humble family background to a high place in the world of business in only a few years. Late in 1878, the nineteen-year-old Insull was working as a clerk for a London auction house when he read a magazine article about thirty-one-year-old Thomas Alva Edison. The inventor seemed to Insull to be the embodiment of all that was dynamic and exciting, and Edison instantly became Insull's hero and inspiration. Within a year, Insull was working for the Edison Telephone Company of Great Britain, Ltd. When Edward H. Johnson, Edison's principal business lieutenant, came to London in 1880 to manage the affairs of the telephone company, he was impressed by Insull's command of detail and cool business daring. Edison's British telephone company was soon to be sold to the Bell interests, and Johnson invited Insull to come to the United States as Edison's private secretary.

In February, 1881, young Insull sailed for New York. Johnson met him at the pier and informed him that Edison would see him at once. Edison was then in the process of closing his headquarters at Menlo Park and moving to New York City. Bags in hand, Insull found himself whisked off to Edison's office in the building of Edison Electric Light at 65 Fifth Avenue. Insull's biographer, Forrest McDonald, writes:

> Insull looked at Edison, and Edison looked at Insull, and both were disappointed; each said to himself, "My God! He's so young!" Insull was twenty-one and looked sixteen; he was skinny, popeyed, fuzzy-cheeked; his dress was impractically impeccable and his manner was impractically formal. His Cockney accent was so thick that Edison had difficulty understanding him. Mouth agape, he stared at his hero. Edison had just turned thirty-four. He wore a seedy black Prince Albert coat and waistcoat, black trousers that looked as if they had been slept in, a large sombrero, a rough brown overcoat, and a white silk handkerchief around his neck, tied in a careless knot and falling over the front of a dirty white shirt. His hair was long and shaggy; he was beardless but ill-shaven. His manner was as casual as Insull's was formal. His middle western accent was so thick that Insull had difficulty understanding him. Over-all, the only saving feature was "the wonderful intelligence and magnetism of his expression, and the extreme brightness of his eyes." But here was the man who had invented the stock ticker, the multiplex telegraph, the mimeograph machine, the phonograph, and the transmitter that made the telephone practical; the man who said he had invented and was about to give to the world electric lighting, electric power, and electric transportation; the man who would invent, in the next decade, the motion picture and discover the principles that made possible radio and television. Despite Edison's appearance, Insull understandably stood awed.

When the formalities were over, Johnson took Insull to the upstairs back room in the office building where he would live. Then they went off for a quick dinner with Mrs. Johnson and Mrs. Edison, and by eight o'clock were back in Edison's office to begin an all-night working session. Insull's first impression was that Edison was "engaged in a gigantic undertaking." The inventor told him of his struggle against the gas companies, his fight to get the equipment he needed, his campaign to obtain a franchise, and even his problems with his own backers. He said that he planned to be employing 1,500 men within a few months. Insull later declared,

> Right after dinner Mr. Edison explained to me that it was necessary for him to start three or four manufacturing establishments to produce dynamos and lamps and underground conductors for his first district. He produced a wallet from his pocket, told me that he had $78,000 to his credit at Drexel, Morgan & Co. and asked me where he could get the balance.

Insull was justifiably bewildered at being admitted so intimately to Edison's financial difficulties so soon after meeting the man. But he sat down beside Johnson—who was departing for Europe before dawn—and began to go over Edison's accounts. By four that morning Insull had drawn up a list of the expected royalty income Edison could borrow against in the next few months, and had worked out with Johnson a program for selling some of Edison's European telephone securities to raise still more money. By five, Johnson was aboard his ship; Insull and Edison caught a few hours' sleep, and after breakfast headed for the East River docks to inspect the Goerck Street building that would soon become the Edison Machine Works. One of Insull's first assignments was to negotiate the purchase of that building. A little later in the day Edison formally hired Insull and offered him a salary of $100 a month. That was half

169

what Insull had been making in London, but he accepted without a murmur. Before long, Edison was loading him down with valuable bonuses in stock.

Insull wrote, more than fifty years later,

> I do not think I had any understanding with Edison when I first went to him as to my duties. I did whatever he told me to, and looked after all kinds of affairs, from buying his clothes to financing his business. I used to open all the correspondence and answer it all, sometimes signing Edison's name with my initials, sometimes signing my own name. . . . I held his power of attorney and signed his checks. It was seldom that Edison signed a letter or a check at that time. . . . Edison would make his own notes on letters and I would be expected to clean up the correspondence with Edison's laconic notes as guide to the character of answer to make. It was a very common thing for Edison to write the word "Yes" or "No" and this would be all I would have.

Insull served his master well. He had a positive gift for borrowing money; and since Edison was determined to plunge deep into debt to finance the electric light business, Insull was kept busy raising loans. It was a task he performed superbly. Much later, he would build his own billion-dollar utility empire mainly on borrowed money, thereby helping to set the stage for one of history's costliest bankruptcies. But that dizzying adventure was not even a dream in 1881. No one could have imagined that such a vast power corporation as Insull would construct could ever exist—let alone that it could fail.

Edison's new headquarters at 65 Fifth Avenue was a large, handsome four-story mansion in a fashionable residential and shopping district. It was "uptown" for 1881—just below Fourteenth Street. Edison took a childish glee in the magnificence of the building. He was quoted in the New York *Tribune* that February as saying, "We're up in the world now! I remember ten years ago—I had just come from Boston—I had to walk the streets of New York all night because I hadn't the price of a bed. And now think of it! I'm to occupy a whole house on Fifth Avenue."

He quickly installed a small steam engine to run a dynamo, and wired the building for electricity. Glittering chandeliers held dozens of electric lights to impress the bankers, politicians, and celebrities who paid calls on the Edison office. The top floor was given over to a classroom in which Edison trained workmen; Insull and a number of engineers slept on the premises; the lower floors were divided between elegantly-appointed conference rooms and laboratories. Edison spent most of his time at 65 Fifth Avenue, occasionally darting out for a quick visit to the lamp factory at Menlo Park or the machine shop on Goerck Street. He generally slept there too, taking his usual brief naps between meetings. His long-neglected family had been installed in a hotel near Gramercy Park, and when his conscience panged him he would visit his wife and three children.

With furious, driving energy, Edison labored all during 1881 to make Edison Illuminating a going concern. To Insull's dismay, the inventor worked night and day with no regard for regularity—sometimes disappearing without warning for a long period of sleep—kept wildly incoherent books, and occasionally departed from his own careful cost accounting to launch into some incredibly wasteful project. Yet there was steady progress.

One of Edison's own chores was to find a site for the First District power station. It had to be centrally located, for operating efficiency's sake, and the land had to be cheap, for the sake of economy. In later autobiographical notes Edison wrote:

> While planning for my first New York station . . . I had no real estate, and from lack of experience had very little knowledge of its cost in New York; so I assumed a rather large liberal amount of it to plan my station on it. It occurred to me one day that before I went too far with my plans I had better find out what real estate was worth. In

my original plan I had 200 by 200 feet. I thought that by going down on a slum street near the waterfront I would get some pretty cheap property. So I picked out the worst dilapidated street there was, and found I could only get two buildings each 25 feet front, one 100 feet deep and the other 85 feet deep. I thought about $10,000 each would cover it; but when I got the price I found that they wanted $75,000 for one and $80,000 for the other. Then I was compelled to change my plans and go upward in the air where real estate was cheaper. I cleared out the building entirely and built my station of structural iron work running it up high.

He purchased the 50-by-100-foot site at 255-57 Pearl Street in August of 1881 for $150,000. There was unconscious irony in Edison's reference to the neighborhood as "the worst dilapidated street there was," for at the beginning of the nineteenth century Pearl Street had been an aristocratic residential thoroughfare. But New York has always been a city of swift transformations.

The work of converting the old buildings into a central power station began at once. A fire wall divided the two four-story buildings. That was left intact. One of the buildings was used to house the generating station, with the boilers on the ground floor, the dynamos and their directly-connected steam engines on the second floor. Iron columns and girders were added to support the weight of this equipment. The adjoining building became a tube shop for construction work.

At the same time Edison workmen were ripping up the streets of the First District to put down the mains and feeders that were to carry the current. Here was the crucial test of the Edison system, for there was little money to waste on mistakes. Fifteen miles of conductors would be needed. The unique Edison system called for the feeders to supply power to mains at central points, instead of starting the huge mains directly at the dynamos, and if executed properly, costs would be held to a minimum. Edison laid out a miniature plan in silver wire first,

basing it on his remarkably accurate "census" of power needs
in the district. So well had this survey been carried out, he said,

> that we could go into a man's store and say: "Your gas bill
> in December was $62.40!" When he looked it up, it was
> usually within 5 per cent of it. We sometimes found that
> our estimates were too small, and I soon discovered the
> cause of this. We went to a place on Sixth Avenue. The
> man's bill ought to have been $16. It was $32. We took a
> delicate meter up there, and found that there was a leak
> which had been going on for fifteen years.

Other electrical engineers were openly skeptical of Edison's
plan for underground power distribution, insisting that all the
current would leak away into the earth. City officials also tried
to discourage him. One remarked, "Some electricians wanted all
the air, Edison asked only for the earth." Edison maintained
that underground lines would not only eliminate a potential
eyesore but would avoid the risks of shock or fire from short
circuits. "Why, you don't lift water pipes and gas pipes on stilts,"
he declared.

At the Washington Street factory of the Electric Tube Company, the indefatigable Kruesi presided over the rapid construction of four and one-half miles of feeders and ten and one-
half miles of mains. Boiling kettles of asphalt and linseed oil
bubbled long hours each day. The conductors were copper bars
20 feet 6 inches long, inserted in 20-foot sections of iron pipe.
The hot asphalt compound was pumped in to provide insulation, and junction boxes were installed between each section of
copper. During the construction work the lengths of tubing
had to be stuck out a front window to turn them around, thus
involving the neighborhood not only in the excitement but in
the odor. It was autumn before the breaking of earth got under
way, and the job of laying the mains was a race against frost.

173

The Irish workmen, Kruesi recalled, were afraid of "the devils in the wires," and had to be reassured by the constant presence of Batchelor, Kruesi, or Edison himself.

Just as the laying of the mains commenced, an inspector from the office of the Commissioner of Public Works halted the work and summoned Edison to see the Commissioner. In Edison's account,

> The Commissioner said to me, "You are putting down these tubes. The Department of Public Works requires that you should have five inspectors to look after this work, and their salary shall be $5 per day, payable at the end of each week. Good morning." I went out very much crestfallen, thinking I would be delayed and harassed in the work which I was anxious to finish, and was doing night and day. We watched patiently for those inspectors to appear. The only appearance they made was to draw their pay Saturday afternoons.

The mains had to be tested before they could be put down. This job was done in the cellar of the unfinished Pearl Street power station, and each night all the untested tubes were stacked against the wall. Workmen often slept in the cellar during the winter of 1881-82 after an overtime session; two of them became fatally ill in those cold, damp surroundings. Edison, too, slept in the cellar, but without harmful effects. One night he, Kruesi, and Batchelor worked so late that all three bedded down there. Kruesi later said,

> There was room on the floor for one, on a work bench for the other. They drew lots and Edison drew third; so he was reduced to lying down for the night on the iron tubes. I remember that he had on a very light-colored suit which, by morning, was marked with streaks of tar from shoulders to feet, for the warmth of his body had softened the tar.

The dynamos that were to provide power for the First District were of a new and improved kind—the largest electrical generators that had ever been built. Edison nicknamed them "Jumbos," after the famed circus elephant of P. T. Barnum. The first Jumbo was constructed not for Pearl Street service but as a display in the Paris Exhibition of 1881; for, in the midst of all his work, Edison did not neglect opportunities for publicity abroad.

As was customary at any of these international expositions, wonders of technology were prominently featured. Edison's contribution was an awesome dynamo that weighed 27 tons, counting its 200-horsepower engine. The armature alone weighed 6 tons; the generating capacity was enough to light 1000 bulbs at once. Packed in 137 crates, the Jumbo was shipped by steamer to France in the summer of 1881. Charles Batchelor served as Edison's representative at the show.

Many types of lighting systems were exhibited: the arc lights of Jablochkoff and Brush, and the incandescent lights of Edison, Swan, Maxim, and Lane-Fox. Only the Edison display, though, was a total system embracing dynamo, distribution lines, hundreds of lamps, and all appliances. It was nothing else than a miniature Edison lighting district, and it had great impact on the viewers. When the awards were bestowed, Batchelor cabled Edison: "Official list published today shows you in highest class in inventors. Swan, Lane-Fox and Maxim receive medals in the class below." Commercial applications were quick to follow; the Société Continentale Edison of France was organized to exploit the lighting patents on the Continent, and soon Batchelor was in charge of a bustling manufacturing firm at Ivry-sur-Seine.

A little later in 1881 Edison acquired a foothold in England as well with the formation of the Edison Electric Lighting Company, Ltd. Swan's incandescent lamps, which were virtually identical in principle to Edison's, were winning wide popularity in England. A notable Swan success was the lighting of the Savoy Theatre in London, which was begun on December 28, 1881—the first instance of a theater lit entirely by electricity.

But Swan could offer only isolated lighting plants; Edison held patents on widespread power distribution from a central station. Edward H. Johnson, who was again serving as Edison's agent in London, gained the approval of the city authorities for the incandescent lighting of the district around Holborn Viaduct. Holborn Viaduct had previously been lighted by 16 Jablochkoff arc lights for six months in 1878 and 1879, but the experiment had been discontinued because of its high cost, and the gas lighting restored. Johnson now proposed to light the Viaduct and adjacent streets for a period of three months at no cost to the municipal government, making power available as well to any private consumers in the vicinity who wished to purchase it. This permission was granted on January 2, 1882.

Almost at once a power station was in operation. Edison had quietly supplied Johnson with dynamos and distribution equipment in anticipation of city approval. He was eager to try out his system in actual commercial use somewhere before it went into service in New York, and London seemed sufficiently far away to minimize the risks of failure. So it was that the world's first commercial incandescent light power station went into service in London on January 12, 1882, nine months before the completion of the Pearl Street station in New York.

The experiment was successful. A 22-ton Jumbo dynamo generated current for 1000 lamps; soon a 1200-lamp unit was added, and then a third dynamo, also of 1200-lamp capacity, followed by a 250-lamp unit for daytime customers. The outdoor lights spread from Holborn Viaduct into adjoining streets, while the owners of the buildings in the area quickly signed up for service. One of the biggest clients secured was the General Post Office, where some four hundred incandescent lamps were installed. At the end of the three-month trial, the city contracted for a continuation of the street-lighting service at the same price it had been paying for gas light. The omens were good for the success of Pearl Street.

176

The London results were reported in detail to Edison, who drew on the experience of Holborn Viaduct to improve the system he was constructing in New York. The three Jumbo dynamos that were installed at Pearl Street in May of 1882 were bigger and more reliable than those that had been built for London. They were rated at a capacity of 1200 lamps, and the direct-connected steam engines were 200-horsepower units that would whirl the armatures at 1200 revolutions per minute. No one had ever operated such immense dynamos before, and not even Edison could predict what would happen when two of the Jumbos were run in tandem.

The big boilers were fired up early in July of 1882, and on July 6 Edison ordered a test of the dynamos. As he told it,

> Finally we got our feeders all down and started to put on an engine and turn over one of the machines to see how things were. My heart was in my mouth at first, but everything worked all right, and we had more than 500 ohms insulation resistance. Then we started another engine and threw them in parallel. Of all the circuses since Adam was born we had the worst then. One engine would stop and the other would run up to about a thousand revolutions, and then they would see-saw.
>
> What was the matter? Why, it was these Porter governors! When the circus commenced the men who were standing around ran out precipitately, and some of them kept running for a block or two. I grabbed the throttle of one engine and E. H. Johnson, who was the only one present to keep his wits, caught hold of the other and we shut them off.

One of those who fled only as far as the end of the dynamo room added,

> It was a terrifying experience, as I didn't know what was going to happen. The engines and dynamos made a horrible racket, from loud and deep groans to a hideous shriek, and

177

the place seemed to be filled with sparks and flames of all
colors. It was as if the gates of the infernal regions had suddenly been opened.

To return to Edison's account:

Of course I discovered then that what had happened was
that one set was running the other one as a motor. I then
put up a long shaft connecting all the governors together,
and thought this would certainly cure the trouble, but it
didn't. The torsion of the shaft was so great that one governor still managed to get ahead of the others. Then I went
to Goerck Street and got a piece of shafting and a tube in
which it fitted. I twisted the shaft one way and the tube the
other as far as I could and pinned them together. In this
way, by straining the whole outfit up to its elastic limit in
opposite directions, the torsion was practically eliminated,
and after that the governors ran together all right.

But they did not run that way for long. Edison feared the
results of putting such an unstable system into day-by-day
operation. At that late date he took the bold step of abandoning
the Porter-Allen steam engines with which he had worked for a
year and a half. He commissioned an engineer named Gardiner
C. Sims to design a new engine that would run at 350 r.p.m. and
give 175 horsepower. Sims swiftly designed two Armington-
Sims engines at his Rhode Island workshop; when installed at
Pearl Street to replace the Porter-Allen engines, they broke
down in the first few minutes of use, but after three weeks of
steady work Sims got his engines to work as Edison wanted
them to do.

By August, about fifty buildings in the First District had
been wired, and more than a thousand incandescent lamps had
been placed in their sockets. No one knew when service would
officially begin, for Edison was warily putting his system
through its final tests. He was hampered by an almost total
absence of control instruments. Pearl Street did not have a

single testing, indicating, or recording device. Each dynamo had its own control switches, as no central switchboard had yet come into existence. When it became apparent that there might be unpredictable voltage variations, Edison rigged a crude voltage indicator: if the pressure got to be one or two volts above the desired force, a red lamp would flash on the dynamo's control panel, and a watching attendant would have to turn a hand wheel to raise the resistance of the circuit; if voltage dipped, a blue lamp was the warning signal to the attendant to cut resistance.

During these final weeks of testing, Edison was besieged by questions—both from reporters and stockholders—concerning the day when service would start. He promised an early commencement. But when he chose the day of the grand opening, he told only his associates. For once, he wanted no publicity until the outcome was certain. He declared eight years later,

> The Pearl Street station was the biggest and most responsible thing I had ever undertaken. It was a gigantic problem, with many ramifications. There was no parallel in the world. . . . All our apparatus, devices and parts were home-devised and home-made. Our men were completely new and without central-station experience. What might happen on turning a big current into the conductors under the streets of New York no one could say. . . . The gas companies were our bitter enemies in those days, keenly watching our every move and ready to pounce upon us at the slightest failure. Success meant world-wide adoption of our central-station plan. Failure meant loss of money and prestige and setting back of our enterprise. All I can remember of the events of that day is that I had been up most of the night rehearsing my men and going over every part of the system. . . . If I ever did any thinking in my life it was on that day.

Edison had selected 3 P.M. on September 4, 1882 to initiate service. The first customer to receive power would be J. P. Morgan; the board members of Edison Illuminating were to gather in the offices of Drexel, Morgan & Co. at 23 Wall Street to watch the lights go on. After that service would be extended to the other initial subscribers. At nine in the morning on the great day Edison arrived at Pearl Street in a frock coat and a white, high-crowned derby. He removed his collar and coat, rolled up his shirtsleeves, and got to work. All morning Edison and his chief electrical engineer, John W. Lieb, gave the equipment its last checkout. Reporters somehow got wind of the imminent event and clustered outside the building; when one slipped through the door, Edison seized him and pushed him bodily out again. He wanted to see no reporters, he said, until after three o'clock.

Edison himself was not going to be present in the dynamo room when the switch was thrown. The plan called for him to go to the Morgan office to greet the directors and witness with them the first glow of light. Since there was no telephone service between Pearl Street and Morgan's Wall Street bank, watches were carefully synchronized to minimize any embarrassing delays. When he was satisfied that all would be well, Edison tensely left the power station and walked the half mile to 23 Wall Street. Lieb remained at Pearl Street to throw in the main circuit breaker and connect the generating unit to the system.

Lieb later wrote,

> If my memory is not altogether at fault, I was deputized to throw the circuit breaker, for I remember distinctly that the handle of the breaker could only be reached by standing on tip-toes, and, as the breaker was thrown in, the catch which held it in place did not engage properly and it was necessary for me to hang on to the breaker while someone obtained a bench to push the catch into its contact.

Among those who waited with Edison and Morgan in the opulent banking office were John Kruesi, Francis Upton, Ed-

180

ward Johnson, Sigmund Bergmann, and Samuel Insull. Charles Batchelor and Francis Jehl, who had had so much to do with the success of the project, were in Europe on business for Edison, as was the devoted Grosvenor Lowrey. There were various members of the overlapping directorates of Edison Electric Light Company and its subsidiary, Edison Electric Illuminating Company, on hand, along with a man from *Scientific American* and a select group of newspaper reporters. The tension rose as the hands of the clock swept toward three. The eyes of the watchers flicked from the unlit lamps to the figure of Edison, who had donned his white derby once again but who had forgotten to put his collar back on before leaving Pearl Street.

One of the directors said, "A hundred dollars the lights don't go on."

"Taken," Edison said, and reached for the switch. The bulbs in Morgan's office came to life.

"They're on!" cried the directors.

"I have accomplished all I promised," said Edison.

eleven

In Business
at Last

SOON the 106 lamps glowing in the Morgan office were joined by those in neighboring buildings. Later that afternoon the 52 lamps in the editorial room of the New York *Times* went on, although, as the *Times* commented the next day,

> It was not until about 7 o'clock, when it began to be dark, that the electric light really made itself known and showed how bright and steady it was. . . . Soft, mellow, grateful to the eye; it seemed almost like writing by daylight.

The *Herald* also had its lights, as did the offices in the Polhemus Building, the Barnes Building, and most of the best stores along Nassau and Fulton Streets.

The *Herald* reported the next day:

> In streets and business places throughout the lower quarter of the city there was a strange glow last night. The dim flicker of gas was supplanted by a steady glare, bright and mellow, which illuminated interiors and shone through windows fixed and unwavering. From the outer darkness these points of light looked like drops of flame suspended from

the jets and ready to fall at every moment. It was the glowing incandescent lamps of Edison used last evening for the first time in the practical illumination of the first of the districts into which the city has been divided. There had been some citizens who claimed the lighting of such a space by such a method an impossibility but the result proved the contrary. Edison was vindicated and his light triumphed.

The *Times* stressed the convenience of the new illumination:

> The whole lamp looks so much like a gas burner surmounted by a shade that nine people out of ten would not have known the rooms were lighted by electricity except that the light was more brilliant than gas and a hundred times steadier. To turn on the light nothing is required but to turn the thumbscrew, no matches are needed, no patent appliances. As soon as it is dark enough to need artificial light, you turn the thumbscrew and the light is there; no nauseous smell, no flicker, no glare.

The *Sun* concentrated on Edison himself, noting his disheveled look and grease-stained derby, and quoting him as saying, "We have a greater demand for light than we can supply at present owing to insufficiency of men to put down the wires. We have to educate the men to the use and management of our machinery."

The growth of Edison Illuminating was steady, though not as spectacular as one might think. By October 1, 1882, Pearl Street was serving 59 customers and 1,284 lamps, with a total load of about 30 kilowatts. On December 1 there were 203 customers; a year later, there were 513, with more than ten thousand lamps in use, and more buildings were being wired every day.

Yet the business of selling isolated lighting plants, which Edison regarded as unsound, grew much faster. J. P. Morgan purchased his own home power plant in the autumn of 1882, setting the boiler and steam engine in a pit in his garden, to the great distress of his neighbors. Not even a fire caused by a short circuit, which did damage to the walls and carpets of his library, diminished his enthusiasm. (When a similar fire broke out in the Vanderbilt mansion at Fifth Avenue and 47th Street, a hysterical Mrs. Vanderbilt had the power plant taken out.) Villard's S.S. *Columbia,* back in 1880, had showed the way for isolated lighting in seagoing vessels, and there were many orders now. Hotels and restaurants and theaters beyond the service area of Pearl Street bought Edison equipment. A hotel in the Adirondacks installed 125 Edison lights in the summer of 1881; the dynamo had to be transported piecemeal on mule-back to an elevation of 3500 feet above sea level.

In Boston, the Bijou Theater signed up for an Edison system, and the inventor himself was on hand when it went into use on December 12, 1882—the first theater installation in the United States. Among the invited celebrities was the Governor of Massachusetts. Edison responded to the festive occasion by dressing formally and smiling at the crowd from his box seat. The performance that night was of the Gilbert and Sullivan operetta, *Iolanthe.* All went smoothly until the intermission. During the second act the lights dimmed. Edison, accompanied by Edward Johnson, rushed to the power plant in the cellar and found that a leak in the steam boiler had caused a drop in pressure. Casting aside silk hats and tails, Edison and Johnson unceremoniously began to shovel coal into the boiler, getting themselves into such a disreputable state that they had to be excused from the speechmaking that followed the show.

By the spring of 1883, there were 334 isolated Edison plants in operation, but Pearl Street was still virtually the only central station in the United States. A second one had opened in Appleton, Wisconsin, just three weeks after Pearl Street—a modest 180-light plant whose dynamo was driven by water power—but otherwise the idea had not caught on. Edison's faith in central stations remained strong. He organized the Thomas A. Edison Construction Department, put Samuel Insull in charge of it, and sent the young Englishman out in mid-1883 to sell and build power stations all over the country. Insull, an adroit salesman, lined up contracts in Piqua and Tiffin, Ohio; Sunbury and Harrisburg, Pennsylvania; Fall River and Brockton, Massachusetts; Newburgh, New York; and two dozen other towns and cities, all within eighteen months. In such large cities as San Francisco, Cleveland, and Philadelphia, where there had been an early commitment to arc lights, local investors were slower to support Edison companies.

Edison thus found himself at work on many fronts in 1883 and 1884. His construction subsidiary was building dozens of central stations, as well as turning out isolated plants by the hundreds, and at the same time he was directly concerned in the daily operations of Edison Illuminating in New York.

There were some odd technical problems in the first weeks of Pearl Street. As Edison told a *Sun* reporter,

> We have only one experienced engineer here now. A man came down from our machine shop in Goerck Street the other day and put his oil can between two conductors. He was a badly frightened man a second later, for the can melted away as quickly as the oil it contained. Another workman, while employed at a wire in Fulton Street, used a screwdriver. He was surprised to see his screwdriver burn away, and returned to the station in great haste to know what was the matter.

A few weeks later, said Edison,

> a policeman rushed in and told us to send an electrician at once up to the corner of Ann and Nassau Streets—some trouble. Another man and I went up. We found an immense crowd of men and boys there in the adjoining streets—a perfect jam. There was a leak in one of our junction boxes and, on account of the cellars extending under the street, the top soil had become charged. Hence, by means of this leak, powerful currents were passing through this layer of moist earth. When I arrived, I saw coming along the street a ragman with a dilapidated old horse, and one of the boys

185

told him to go over on the other side of the road, which was the place where the current leaked. When the ragman heard this, he took that side at once. The moment the horse struck the electrified soil, he stood straight up in the air, and then reared again; and the crowd yelled, the policemen yelled; and the horse started to run away. One man who had seen it came to me next day and wanted me to put in apparatus for him at a place where they sold horses. He said he could make a fortune with it, because he could get old nags in there and make them act like thoroughbreds.

Fixture insulators were unknown. The customary process of installing the new lamps involved twining and taping the wires to the old gas chandeliers, and then connecting them to the lamp sockets screwed under the gas burners. Frequently sparks flew in vivid pyrotechnical displays, particularly when static electricity built up in the wires during thunderstorms. When the town of Sunbury, Pennsylvania got its Edison central station in the summer of 1883, there was a particularly awe-inspiring burst of sparks at the City Hotel during a severe storm. The shower of sparks nearly sent the hotel's guests stampeding in panic into the rain. An Edison engineer named William S. Andrews calmed the crowd, but the next day the hotel's proprietor demanded the removal of the wires. In a brilliant improvisation Andrews replied, "You may not realize it, but your hotel was struck by lightning yesterday. If it hadn't been for us you'd be proprietor this morning of nothing but a heap of ashes. Those sparks were the lightning being shunted into the ground on our wires."

"Well!" the proprietor exclaimed in surprise. "If that's the case, we'll let the wires stay, of course."

Soon after that, one of Edison's men, Luther Stieringer, devised an insulated ceiling block for mounting incandescent lights, and the terrifying sparks ceased to fly.

The weather had its effects at Pearl Street, too. Early in 1883 Edison added the New York Stock Exchange as a customer, and thereby found himself contracted to sell somewhat more power all told than Pearl Street could generate at any one time. It was the first, though not the last, time that a power company took on so many customers that it was left with no reserve capacity. Building new dynamos took time and money; at the moment Edison was short of both. He trusted to luck that a time would not come when all his customers were demanding power simultaneously.

The sun was shining brightly one afternoon in late spring, and few offices were using their lights. Then a dark cloud rolled over New York City as a storm approached. The lights in the First District began to go on.

Edison was at 65 Fifth Avenue. He telephoned Pearl Street and asked about the load. The only measure of output then was a primitive device called an ampere-meter, which was a steam gauge that kept track of the engine's activity. The man on duty checked the ampere-meter and reported, "We are up to the muzzle and everything is running all right."

"By and by," goes Edison's account, "it became so thick we couldn't see across the street. I telephoned again and felt something would happen, but fortunately it did not. I said to Chinnock, 'How is it?' He replied: 'Everything is red-hot and the ampere-meter has made seventeen revolutions!' " But the power did not fail.

Soon afterward, another heavy surge of demand in the First District caused fuses to overheat and blow on the Broad Street feeder. Moments later all the feeders supplying the financial community had blown, and New York City was plunged into its first power failure. The agitated directors of Edison Illuminating, fearing for their investment, rushed to Pearl Street and demanded an instant resumption of service. A couple of spare feeders were found, connected to the system, and used to supply Broad Street. The lights went on; but all over the First District the best anyone got was a dull red glow, for voltage was

187

still low. At the insistent prodding of the financiers, Edison's men quickly brought up the voltage, with the inevitable result: the spare feeders also blew. As torrential rain descended, Edison employees picked their way through the First District to replace every fuse, and several hours passed before the lights went on again.

Such difficulties as these kept Edison's mind away from pettier matters, such as, for example, whether Edison Electric Illuminating Company of New York happened to be operating at a profit. It was not until February of 1883, almost six months after service had begun at Pearl Street, that regular charges were made. Edison said of this period,

> We were not very commercial. We put many customers on, but did not make out many bills. After the Station had been running several months and was a technical success, we began to look after the financial part. We started to collect some bills; but we found that our books were kept very badly, and that the person in charge, who was no business man, had neglected that part of it. So I got the directors to permit me to hire a man to run the Station.

The man Edison had hired was Charles E. Chinnock, the able and efficient superintendent of the Metropolitan Telephone Company of New York. Chinnock had not been eager to leave his job for an unknown future at Pearl Street, but was persuaded to come over by Edison's offer of a bonus of $10,000 if he could raise the profits of the power station to a level of 5 per cent return on its capitalization of $600,000. Chinnock achieved that in short order, but the officers and directors of Edison Electric Light refused to honor the agreement, claiming that Edison lacked the authority to enter into such irregular bonus arrangements. As Edison commented, "They said they 'were sorry'—that is, 'Wall Street sorry'—and refused to pay it. This shows what a nice, generous lot of people they have over in

188

Wall Street." Edison paid Chinnock's $10,000 out of his own pocket.

At the outset Edison had hoped to bill his customers at a flat rate per lamp, regardless of power consumption. But this was clearly inequitable and unworkable, and before Pearl Street opened Edison had invented the first electric meter. It was an elegantly simple device that relied on the process of electrolysis—that is, the ability of an electric current to break down chemical substances. The Edison meter was a glass cell containing two small plates of chemically pure zinc in a bath of zinc sulphate. When the customer used power, a fraction of the current entering his premises was diverted to flow through the meter from the positive plate to the negative. A certain amount of zinc was removed from the first plate and deposited on the second, in proportion to the amount of current used. To calculate power consumption, one merely had to check the weight of the plates each month.

The Edison meter worked remarkably well, so long as the zinc sulphate solution remained liquid, but in cold weather the chemical would freeze and knock out the meter. Said Edison,

> I set to work to negative this difficulty, and succeeded, as I thought, by putting an incandescent lamp in each meter with a thermostat strip, which would make a contact through the lamp when the temperature fell to 40 degrees. That idea, simple as it was, caused us a whole lot of trouble. The weather became cold, and then the telephone in our office began to ring every five minutes and people would say—
> "Our meter's red hot. Is that all right?"
> Then someone else would call up and say—
> "Our meter's on fire inside, and we poured water on it. Did that hurt it?"

Meter-reading was carried on in a lackadaisical way through the fall of 1882. Things changed when Chinnock took over,

189

however. He had a payroll to meet—there were seventy-eight employees at Pearl Street when it opened, receiving aggregate pay of $71,000.80 a year—and the bills for coal and copper mounted as the roster of customers grew. So a weighing crew began making the rounds in a horse-drawn wagon. The old meter plates were collected and tagged for weighing, and new plates were inserted in the meters. The first bill for lighting based on Edison meter readings was collected on January 18, 1883, from the Ansonia Brass & Copper Company of Cliff Street: $50.40. By February all customers were receiving bills.

Among those who distrusted the meters was J. P. Morgan. As a stockholder, Morgan relished the thought of high electric bills for the customers; as a customer himself, he did not feel quite the same way. When a meter was installed at 23 Wall Street, the great banker decided to keep his own tally. Cards were printed and hung on each electric fixture in the Morgan office. Every employee had instructions to note on the card the exact times at which the lamp was turned on and off. (Such concepts as "kilowatts" and "kilowatt hours" were not yet in existence; billings were based simply on the "lamp hours" used by each fixture per month.)

When the first bill came in, Morgan checked it against the cards and found an apparent overcharge. Chuckling tolerantly, he called it to Edison's attention. "Give the little beggar another chance," said Edison. The second month's bill showed another overcharge, a substantial one, and this time Morgan did not chuckle quite so graciously. Edison undertook a personal investigation of the discrepancy. He went over the Drexel, Morgan & Co. office, assuring himself that the meter and all the fixtures and wires were in good order. He examined the meticulous hourly records of the bank clerks who used the lamps. Then he asked who did the chores after dark. A janitor, he was told—"really a very excellent chap." The excellent chap was

190

sent for. Edison asked him what light he used while swabbing the floors at night, and the janitor pointed to a central fixture carrying ten lamps. Naturally, he had made no record of power use while tidying up in the bright glow of the Edison light. The following month, the janitor also kept records of his use of the lights, and the meter total was virtually identical with that on Morgan's cards. After that, the cards disappeared, and Morgan became a vocal admirer of the Edison meter.

Though the meter was reliable, the human beings who read it were subject to ordinary human fallibility. Thus, when Edison light came to Sunbury, Pennsylvania, the meter in a large clothing store showed a power consumption of $200 one month—far above normal. The horrified meter reader brooded over this for two nights before he found the error. In order to fit a new set of plates into the meter-box he had clipped off an inch or two of copper wire, forgetting that he had previously weighed the plates, wire and all. The loss in weight represented by the absent wire had rung up an extra debit of $150 on the customer's account.

The shorter days of winter produced an increase in power use—and in the monthly bill—and this perturbed some customers. Edison recalled,

> I remember one man who had a saloon on Nassau Street. He had had his lights burning for two or three months. It was in June, and Chinnock put in a bill for $20; July for $20; August about $28; September about $35. Of course, the nights were getting longer. October about $40; November about $45. Then the man called Chinnock up. He said: "I want to see you about this electric light bill." Chinnock went up to see him. He asked: "Are you the manager of this electric light plant?" Chinnock replied, "I have the honor." "Well," he stated, "my bill has gone from $20 up to $28, $35, $45. I want you to understand, young fellow, that my limit is $60.

191

The chemical meters soon were accepted without question. They remained in universal use until 1896, when the first version of today's mechanical meter was developed by Elihu Thomson. The transition to the new meter came slowly; on September 1, 1898, for instance, Edison Illuminating was serving 4874 chemical meters and 5619 mechanical meters. But by the turn of the century most of the Edison meters were gone.

Chinnock's success in putting Pearl Street on a paying basis is reflected in the quarterly earning figures of Edison Illuminating—which also show the effects of seasonal fluctuations in the use of power:

	1883	1884
January–March	$6,115.84 loss	$10,429.46 profit
April–June	6,040.39 loss	7,251.57 profit
July–September	491.70 profit	3,873.46 profit
October–December	7,207.03 profit	11,669.32 profit
Full year	$4,457.50 net loss	$33,233.81 net profit

By August 1, 1885, Edison Illuminating was able to pay its first dividend—twenty-five cents on each share of $100 par common stock. Most of this went to the parent Edison Electric Light, which owned a heavy interest in the operating subsidiary. The growth in Edison Illuminating's profitability was based on three factors. One was Chinnock's ability to keep things running smoothly. Another was the greater life of the bulbs now being produced at the Edison Lamp Works, for at that time the lighting company had to supply replacement bulbs free of charge. Bulbs had lasted an average of 400 hours in 1883, but by 1885 Edison had reached a figure of 1347 hours per lamp. The third factor was the one that governs power-company economics to this day: generating and distributing equipment is an overwhelming initial capital expense, but additional customers can be connected to the lines without incurring correspondingly large further expenses. Thus a new company must bear an enormous capital cost per customer, until the increase in customers spreads these costs out thinly enough to bring down the ratio of capital expended to customers served. With the same dynamos at Pearl Street serving an ever greater number of customers, Chinnock's return on capital improved daily.

But there are limits to that sort of improvement. A time comes when new generating equipment must be added to meet the growing load, and the capital cycle begins again. The expansion of Edison Illuminating beyond Pearl Street was hampered by the timidity of Edison's always wary backers to make expansion capital available.

Edison had planned a string of central stations serving all of Manhattan. In his early New York work he laid out thirty-six power districts south of 59th Street, each to have its own generating plant. That seemed to him to be the minimum number of stations for Manhattan service, since his distributing system worked efficiently only at distances of less than a mile; beyond that, unavoidable voltage drops set in, making impossible any such glamorous notion as a single huge station serving the entire city. But when he proposed to the directors that they raise funds for new Manhattan power stations, they balked. Not until 1888 did Edison Illuminating get its second and third generating plants.

One cause of their caution was the threat of competition, both from gas companies and from other electric companies. The six gas companies of New York City, by their peace treaty of 1880, had been able to end their rate war and return to a profitable basis. Now they met the Edison threat by a merger that would allow them to cut their rates and remain profitable through operating economies. On September 16, 1884, the merger terms were drawn up. Six weeks later the new corporation, Consolidated Gas Company of New York, was organized at the offices of the former Manhattan Gas Light Company, 4 Irving Place. Consolidated Gas's first official act was to cut the price of gas lighting in New York from $2.25 to $1.75 per thousand cubic feet.*

In electric lighting, Brush was still a determined competitor. Wherever it was possible for this arc light firm to get an outdoor contract, Edison Illuminating lost potential business. On April 18, 1884, the New York City Department of Public Works awarded a contract to Brush for the lighting of seventeen parks and thoroughfares—requiring 475 arc lamps in all. Another arc light company had been organized in New York in 1883: the United States Illuminating Company. It specialized at first in the renting of isolated generating plants to private concerns, but its first central power station, in the basement of the Equitable Building at 120 Broadway, was uncomfortably close to the boundaries of Edison's franchised service area. And when the Brooklyn Bridge opened on May 24, 1883, it was lighted by 70 arcs operated by the United States Illuminating Company and supplied from a power station at the Brooklyn end of the bridge. A year later, United States Illuminating was given a contract for 300 outdoor lights in the parks and along the principal north-south thoroughfares below 14th Street. Yet another new arc company was formed in Brooklyn in 1883, the Citizens Electric Illuminating Company of Brooklyn, followed shortly by the Municipal Electric Light Company, which obtained a franchise for an adjoining Brooklyn district.

The loss of all these territories to the arc light was serious enough for Edison, but there was a matter of much greater concern. Competitive incandescent light companies were emerging!

Edison, of course, had filed patent applications on every aspect, no matter how minor, of his electrical system. But filing

* On the principle of joining enemies if they can't be beaten, Consolidated Gas bought control of the Edison Electric Illuminating Company in 1901, long after Edison had left the field. The merged companies eventually adopted the name, Consolidated Edison Company of New York; the main offices are still at 4 Irving Place.

an application is not the same thing as being granted a patent, and some of Edison's most important applications remained "pending" all through the 1880's while bureaucrats debated. Moreover, even a granted patent is nothing more than a license to sue infringers. If Edison had gone after everyone who transgressed on his patent rights, he would have spent the rest of his life in courtrooms.

So the competition developed. Some companies, frankly opportunistic, simply helped themselves to Edison's patents and hoped he would not sue. Others kept their consciences clean by delving into gray areas where rival patent applications left no one, not even Edison, with a clear title to an invention. Among the latter was the Brush Electric Company. In the summer of 1883 Brush obtained the American rights to Joseph Swan's incandescent lamp. The Brush idea was to combine arc and incandescent lighting through the use of storage batteries. Brush connected the batteries to a large dynamo used for powering arc lights; during the day, the dynamo charged the batteries, and at night it ran the arc lights while the incandescent lights on the same system drew their current from the charged batteries. In this way Brush could illuminate a street and the interiors of adjacent houses simultaneously. Soon those areas that had Brush service were getting non-Edison incandescent lights.

Edison did not attempt to sue, partly because his lawyers were uncertain that the Brush-Swan light really was an infringement, and partly because he hoped to triumph through the innate superiority of his system, without the need for expensive litigation. But in England his subsidiary, Edison Electric Lighting Company, Ltd., had begun an infringement suit against Swan's United Electric Light Company early in 1882.

That suit became an academic matter later the same year when Parliament passed a strikingly foolish act permitting any

English town or city to purchase by condemnation a local private power company within a period of twenty-one years, on terms that amounted to compulsory confiscation. That law put a quick end to most private-enterprise electric developments in England, including Edison's, and he was easily persuaded to sell out to Swan. The patent suit was halted and negotiations began on a merger.

A serious obstacle arose at once. Swan's backers wished to include Swan's name—along with Edison's—in the title of the new corporation. To Edison that seemed tacit recognition of the merit of Swan's patent claim, and he would not have it. He declared vehemently that

> the company shall be called the Edison Electric Light Company, Ltd., or at least shall be distinguished by my name *without the name of any other inventor in its title.* The Company may put forward the fact that it is the owner of the Edison, Swan . . . or other patents.

Edison added a disclaimer of priority that does not altogether ring true:

> The last condition is made solely upon business grounds of great importance to me of wishing to distinguish myself as against Mr. Swan. . . . I leave out of view the fact that he and I are disputing the claim to the lamp. The property which this company is to own and operate is an *electric lighting system* to which I have contributed inventions as indispensable as the lamp, my title to which is not, as I understand, disputed anywhere.

Edison's letter included one statement that was later to return in another context, after the consolidation of his companies into General Electric:

> I am bound by pride of reputation, by pride and interest in my work. You will hardly expect me to remain interested,

196

to continue working to build up my new inventions and improvements for a business in which my identity has been lost. . . .

But at last he gave way. On October 26, 1883, the Edison & Swan United Electric Light Company, Ltd., came into being. For a while it attempted to continue in England as a power company, until the repressive workings of the new law made that impractical; then it concentrated chiefly on manufacturing, producing a light bulb sold under the Ediswan label.

Swan no longer posed a competitive threat to Edison, except as the licenser of the Brush-Swan incandescent system in the United States. Yet instantly a new challenger appeared: the Thomson-Houston Electric Company.

Elihu Thomson and Edwin Houston, the two electrically-minded Philadelphia professors, had assigned their patents in arc lighting to a New Britain, Connecticut firm, the American Electric Company. But American Electric, though it won some arc light contracts in New England, never really got off the ground. Its chief backer died in 1881, about a year after the company was formed, and its growth halted. By the spring of 1882 American Electric was on the market. Control passed to a syndicate of businessmen from Lynn, Massachusetts, led by a successful young shoe manufacturer named Charles A. Coffin. Coffin renewed the agreement with Thomson and Houston, and on February 12, 1883, the old American Electric Company was reorganized under the name of the Thomson-Houston Electric Company.

Thomson-Houston, combining the technical skill of its two "electricians" (as electrical engineers were then called) with Coffin's business genius, soon was blossoming. When it was organized it held contracts to supply power for 365 arc lamps on five generating systems. Within a year, it had thirty-one generating stations in operation, serving 2400 arc lamps. Then it went into incandescent lighting. Elihu Thomson designed a system for distributing power that vaguely skirted the Edison claims; since Edison had not yet been granted a patent on his system it was safe to run the risk of suit. The one basic patent that Edison did have was on his incandescent light. Thomson-Houston got around this by purchasing rights to the Sawyer-Man lamp, whose patent status vis-a-vis the Edison lamp had never been made clear in the courts. (Sawyer himself had taken to drink, was arrested on a manslaughter charge in 1883, and died in prison while awaiting trial.)

In 1884 Thomson-Houston began the manufacture of incandescent lamps and the sale of lighting service. The Sawyer-Man lamp that was the core of its system made use of a filament of carbonized bamboo within a vacuum, just as did the Edison lamp. Sawyer's main innovation consisted of a technique of "flashing" the filament by placing it in gasoline vapor and passing a current through it before sealing it in its bulb; this deposited a coating of graphite on it and lengthened its life. "Flashing" was a clear improvement on Edison's manufacturing method, making the Thomson-Houston bulbs more marketable than Edison's. But every other step in the process Edison considered to be an infringement on his own ideas.

During 1883 and 1884, then, Edison was compelled to watch a progressive nibbling away of his potential lighting market by competitors, while the financiers who controlled his patents refused to put up capital for the promotion and expansion of the Edison system. In 1883 *Electrical World* quoted him as saying that he alone "could take hold and push the system. . . . I have come to the conclusion that my system of lighting having been perfected should be promoted. . . . It is all so complicated that I do not like trusting it to new and untried hands; *because science and dollars are so mixed up in it.*"

twelve

Troubled
Years

THE anxieties and demands of his electrical work had left Edison virtually a stranger to his family since the fall of 1878. He had never been much of a family man, generally preferring the surroundings of his workshop and the company of his associates, but in the early Menlo Park years he had always been able to break away from time to time to perform the functions of husband and father. Once he became committed to the electric light and took on responsibilities to outside investors, such as he had not had in his days as an independent researcher, he often did not come home for weeks on end. One Menlo Park neighbor reported seeing him arriving after a prolonged spell of laboratory work, "coming up the plank path to his house walking as though he were asleep."

Mary Edison, a placid and uncomplicated woman, apparently raised no objections to this sort of relationship. She was lonely, yes, but she had for company the wives of Batchelor, Kruesi, and Upton, and for a while her own unmarried sister, Alice Stilwell. In time Alice married and moved away. By then Mary Edison had children to occupy her time: her daughter Marion, born in 1872, Thomas A. Edison, Jr., born in 1876, and William, born in 1878. Then, too, Mary led a comfortable life, with a handsome home and a staff of servants, and she had acquired reflected fame as the wife of one of the country's best-known men. So there were certain consolations for her husband's single-minded dedication to work.

When he was with his family Edison showed little warmth. His nearly total deafness was a barrier to communication, and he seemed wounded that neither of his sons showed any interest in engineering. Edison's attentions to his children often took the form of designing mischievous and playfully cruel toys for them: a glass swan, for example, that sprayed a child with water when he blew into it in a certain way. But he was not often malicious nor entirely indifferent; at unpredictable moments Edison was warmly affectionate. He could also show a fierce temper. At best he was a difficult man to live with.

Late in 1883 he fell ill, probably under the fatigue of getting Pearl Street going, and during the winter went with his wife and daughter to northern Florida. It was the first of many winter trips Edison would make to Florida, but the only one with his wife Mary. After the Edisons returned to New York early in 1884, he returned to the problems of the light company, and his wife returned to her quiet life of tea parties and other genteel social amusements. When the weather grew warm she moved back to Menlo Park, which had been a summer home for the Edisons since their transplantation to New York City in 1881. There she contracted typhoid fever in July, and there she died on August 9, 1884.

The death of his young wife, so unexpected, so swift, was a shattering blow to Edison. Those who were close to him said that he was never the same afterward—that his spirit of youthful optimism vanished, that he became cautious, conservative, hesitant. None of his inventions after 1884 was of major scope to compare with the phonograph or the electric light, save only the motion picture; most of his work after that time amounted to small refinements of earlier projects, and the bigger enterprises tended to be trivial in nature or else disastrously foolish. It was not that Mary Edison had acted in any way as an advisor to Edison, for at best she had only a dim idea of what he did in his workshop. But somehow she stabilized him, kept him on course and moving forward. When he married again a year and a half later, he chose a far more intelligent and dynamic woman for his bride, yet she never managed to re-kindle whatever spark it was that had gone out that August day in 1884.

Edison soothed his grief in work: work and more work, for there was plenty to be done. He abandoned Menlo Park entirely, allowing its buildings to fall into ruin. His laboratory had already been transferred to New York City. Now he closed his Menlo Park home as well. The factory of the Edison Lamp Company had been moved to Harrison, New Jersey in April, 1882. The wizard had no links left to the scene of his greatest triumphs.

The work that he plunged into during this time of mourning was modest in nature. He drew back from deeper exploration of an accidental discovery of earlier years, the so-called "Edison effect," that might under other circumstances have led him to the practical development of radio transmission.

As far back as February of 1880, Edison had noticed that his incandescent bulbs tended to become blackened, evidently through deposit of carbon particles on the inside of the glass. Study showed that the heat of incandescence boiled these particles from the filament and in some fashion carried them to the inner surface of the bulb. Interestingly, one leg of the horseshoe-shaped filament cast a "shadow" on the bulb—a narrow white streak in the blackened area—as though that leg were intercepting some of the carbon particles before they could hit the glass. The leg that cast this shadow was always the one connected to the positive side of the direct-current circuit supplying the lamp. Edison reasoned that the negative leg of the filament must be the one giving off the particles.

201

Work on Pearl Street kept him away from this examination for two years. By the summer of 1882 it had occurred to him that the carbon particles must certainly carry a negative electrical charge themselves, and that they could be attracted to a positively charged plate placed between the electrodes of the filament. When he had such a bulb built, he was able to detect a current flowing *without wires* from the negative electrode to the positive plate; when he put a negative charge on the plate, no current flowed. He had discovered a method for wireless transmission of current through a vacuum.

It seemed to have no special commercial use, but he filed a patent application for the bulb with the added plate anyway, on November 15, 1883.

> I have discovered that if a conducting substance is interposed anywhere in the vacuous space within the globe of an incandescent electric lamp, and said conducting substance is connected outside the lamp with one terminal, preferably the positive one of the incandescent conductor, a portion of the current will, when the lamp is in operation, pass through the shunt-circuit thus formed, which shunt includes a portion of the vacuous space within the lamp. The current I have found to be proportional to the degree of incandescence of the conductor or candle power of the lamp.

The Edison-effect lamp received its first public showing at an electrical exposition in Philadelphia in September, 1884. Edwin J. Houston was impressed with the "high vacuum phenomena observed by Mr. Edison" and remarked, "I am inclined to believe that we may possibly have here a new source of electrical excitement." Edison had already found a use for the bulb: as an indicator of voltage change in his incandescent light circuits. But as his dark mood of mourning overtook him that autumn, he put the puzzling lamp aside and never returned to it.

It remained for other men to discover that currents of electricity were composed of incredibly small negatively-charged particles called *electrons*, and that Edison's 1883 bulb was actually a device that regulated the flow of electrons through a vacuum. It was, in fact, the first electronic instrument: an early version of the diode, or two-element vacuum tube. By the first decade of the twentieth century Lee de Forest had gone on to interpose a wire grid between the positive and negative electrodes, creating the triode, which made possible the amplification of radio waves and the development of modern electronics. All this might have fallen to Edison, a generation earlier, if he had cared to pursue the implications of his startling discovery that an electrical current could flow through a vacuum.

Another Edison invention of his last really fertile year, 1883, was the three-wire system of electrical transmission. He had begun working this out in November of 1882, too late to use it at Pearl Street, and gave it its first practical test during the construction of the Sunbury, Pennsylvania power system in the summer of 1883.

Under the original two-wire system, one wire running from the dynamo was positive and one negative, with the lamps wired between them like rungs on a ladder, each operating independently. Edison—with the help of an engineer named William S. Andrews and a British mathematician named John Hopkinson—conceived a scheme whereby two 110-volt dynamos were connected in series and three wires were run from them. The outside two were the positive and negative wires; the middle one was neutral. 110-volt lamps were wired to the neutral wire on one side and to one of the outer wires on the other. The neutral wire served as the positive leg of the circuit for lamps connected between the negative wire and the neutral. For lamps connected between the positive wire and the neutral, the neutral wire served as the negative leg of the circuit. The result, in effect, was a super-ladder with three legs and a double set of rungs. With 50 per cent more wire, Edison could run twice as many lamps, and in practice the copper saving was even greater than that. At the same time it became possible to double the working voltage, sending out 220 volts while keeping the lamps at 110, and thereby lessening the inevitable energy loss over distance.

Sunbury's three-wire system was installed by Andrews and a new young Edison engineer, Frank J. Sprague. In this small town there was no need for expensive underground installation, and the power lines were strung overhead on poles. Later in 1883, Sprague supervised the installation of the first underground three-wire system, and took the opportunity to refine some of Edison's equipment. Sprague's new design for a variable-resistance feeder was duly patented and assigned to the Edison Electric Light Company; for Edison it was a useful lesson in what a college-trained engineer could accomplish.

Today the three-wire system is standard on utility installations, and has played a vital role in the expansion of electric service. But the transition to its use was slow; New York City still had some two-wire systems as late as 1902.

The advantages of electricity gained great recognition during 1884 as the Edison system and its several competitors extended their range. Chicago, Boston, Detroit, Cincinnati, and other large cities were opening companies for incandescent lighting, and isolated generating plants also were selling well. From Cambridge, Massachusetts, came news that Gore Hall, the Harvard library, had been given electric lights. A newspaper said:

> This has been a step demanded for years by both professor and student. By the rules of the library the building is open from nine A.M. till half an hour before sunset. In the short winter days this gives a ridiculously small time for using the books. By such a regulation the usefulness of the library has been seriously crippled. The fear of fire prevented the introduction of gas, while the electric light was kept out on the very forcible plea of expense. This latter difficulty has now been remedied. For some time efforts have been made to

collect a sum of money sufficient to defray expenses, which was placed at $2,000. The sum is now secured, and the incandescent light will be introduced in a very short time. No longer will the 300,000 volumes which the library contains be closed to the student on the setting of the sun.

Cleveland now had an electric railway system; the fall of 1884 saw an "electric parade" on New York's Fifth Avenue, with several hundred marchers wearing helmets surmounted by glowing bulbs powered from a portable Edison dynamo; the radiant glow was seen everywhere in the land. But for Edison these developments were tempered by his personal grief and by the growing friction between him and his financial backers. He was having serious trouble with the Morgan group.

Edison had promoted the founding of central power stations outside New York City without the help or encouragement of Edison Electric Light. It was up to Edison, through his salesman Insull, to get the local utilities started. Once they were going concerns, of course, Edison Electric Light stepped in to collect its share of royalties on the Edison patents.

The problem for the local companies was one of capital. It was clear to all that the electrical industry demanded an unusually high initial capital investment—between $4 and $8 for each dollar of gross sales. Although a power company once established would continue to grow steadily at a rate of some six to eight per cent a year, thus doubling its sales in about a decade, the capital investment would have to grow nearly as fast.

New York City's fledgling power company had been financed by J. P. Morgan, but there were few capitalists around the country with anything like his resources. For the sake of getting the industry launched, Edison authorized extremely liberal terms. His Insull-run Thomas A. Edison Construction Department would accept the notes, bonds, and common stock of the new utilities in lieu of cash. Edison Machine Works likewise was

205

willing to take a minimum of cash and a maximum of securities for the dynamos and other heavy equipment it supplied. These policies horrified the officers of Edison Electric Light, who felt that the new local utilities should raise their own capital and should pay for equipment in cash, within thirty days.

Edison's liberality caused him severe problems. His coffers began to bulge with the unmarketable securities and notes of little power companies, while he had to pay cash himself for labor and raw materials. The drain on his capital was immense. To stay solvent, he continued to borrow and to sell off his remaining shares in Edison Electric Light, until his once-controlling stake in the holding company was all but gone.

Then came a change in his fortunes as the power companies left the construction stage and began to do business with the public. They started to turn slender profits and to pay for their additional equipment in cash. Edison still held a great pile of securities of uncertain value, but now he was also earning a handsome return in his accessory-supply companies, which he and his private partners owned independent of Edison Electric Light. The holding company, which had not deigned to finance these manufacturing companies in 1880, began looking longingly at them in 1884. The Morgan group saw profits pouring into the Edison Machine Works and its related firms, and also saw Edison, through the stock he had accepted, getting a grip on dozens of power companies throughout the nation. In July of 1884 the financiers made an attempt to gain control of Edison's manufacturing companies.

The overtures came through Grosvenor Lowrey, who more and more had drifted away from Edison and into the Morgan camp. Lowrey proposed to Edison that the holding company receive "a suitable interest in, and large influence over, the manufacturing business." This was to be done by exchanging stock in Edison Electric Light for 40 per cent interests in the Edison Machine Works, the Edison Lamp Company, Bergmann and Company, and some lesser makers of appliances of fixtures that had been organized.

Edison was infuriated. He had borne all the risks himself, and now that his companies were successful, the financiers, no longer content to receive only modest patent royalties, were offering to step in and share the profits!

Fiery young Samuel Insull goaded Edison to the point of open rupture with the Wall Street men. It was Insull who had had the wearying job of raising the money on which the manufacturing companies had been founded; he had virtually come to identify himself with Thomas Edison and his struggles, and he took the purchase offer as a personal affront. Insull had also been carrying on a private feud with S. B. Eaton, a lawyer who had succeeded Norvin Green as president of Edison Electric Light in 1882. Eaton on some occasion had reprimanded Insull for some minor bit of deviousness, and Insull quietly had sworn to get revenge. Now Insull came to Edison with a scheme for a palace revolution: they would throw Eaton out and gain control of Edison Electric Light themselves.

Insull's idea involved that most dramatic of Wall Street maneuvers, the proxy battle. Edison and his friends held only a minority interest in the holding company, as did the Morgan group. But enough outsiders had purchased Edison Electric Light stock so that the original backers had less than a 50 per cent interest. Morgan owned sufficient stock to control the company under normal circumstances, but if Edison could use his prestige to gain the proxy votes of the independent stockholders, he could outvote Morgan in a showdown.

The split broke into the open in the autumn of 1884. The newspapers, in their financial gossip columns, spoke of the two factions in the Edison organization—"one slow and conservative, the other, including the inventor, energetic and willing to spend money for the sake of making money," as the *Tribune* said late in October, adding, "The result has been, as Mr.

Edison himself put it, that his light has not been used on anything like the scale he might reasonably expect."

Edison's involvement in the proxy fight helped to distract him from his mourning. He had always enjoyed a good fight, and now he was in the fight of his life. He issued Insull-inspired statements denouncing the pomposity of Edison Electric's President Eaton and the go-slow tactics of the board of directors. He called for Eaton's replacement by Edward Johnson, and for a more vigorous approach toward the promotion of local light and power companies, before the unscrupulous, patent-infringing competitors ran away with much of the business.

To his delight Edison found that he had many supporters. One stockholder told him that the company "seemed to have been managed with imbecility, or worse." Proxies began to arrive, though there were some cautionary notes, as this from Edison's old friend, Professor Barker: "I am sorry at this collision. If you win, your capitalists are alienated, and if they win you are dissatisfied."

The board of directors met on October 28, 1884. Edison and Insull arrived with proxies representing slightly more than 50 per cent of the voting stock. The Morgan faction did its best to effect a graceful surrender without suffering total defeat. Through a compromise, the despised Eaton was deposed, and an elderly nonentity named Eugene Crowell was made president. Edward Johnson, Edison's man, became executive vice-president, and, in effect, the acting president, since Crowell was no more than a figurehead. Several Morgan men were dropped from the board of directors—including Grosvenor Lowrey, now fully a member of the conservative faction—and were replaced by Edison partisans. Edison had taken charge. Insull said, "There is no one more anxious after wealth than Samuel Insull, but there are times when revenge is sweeter than money."

Morgan continued to be banker to the firm, and several of

his partners sat on the board of directors. He would still have a voice in affairs—a strong one. But there would be new policies, and there was no more talk of a takeover of the manufacturing companies by the holding company.

Under the Eaton management, Edison Electric Light had been extremely reluctant to launch patent suits against the other firms that had begun to sell incandescent lighting. The holding company simply had not wanted to take the time and trouble to go to court. The slackness of its attitude was made clear in the annual report for 1883:

> The Edison patents, as a matter of law, not only endow our Company with a monopoly of incandescent lighting, but aside from the patents, our business has obtained such a start, one so far in advance of all competitors . . . that the business ascendancy is of itself sufficient to give us a practical monopoly. The one or two . . . competitors have thus far failed to make it worth while for our Company, in the opinion of your Board . . . to go to the expense of bringing suits for infringement.

This view was shared by Edison, who had had too much bitter experience in such litigation. "A lawsuit is the suicide of time," he once noted in his diary. He had come to think it was almost pointless to bother about patents at all—this from the man who had taken out hundreds of them!

Edward Johnson, now that he was the chief executive of Edison Electric Light, took a more vigorous attitude toward infringement. On May 23, 1885, he served public notice on Edison's behalf that the inventor's patent rights would be strongly defended. Two suits were begun at once: one against a firm called the Consolidated Electric Light Company, which owned the Sawyer-Man lamp patents and was licensing them to Thomson-Houston, and the other against the United States Electric Lighting Company, which controlled the Maxim lamp patents and licensed them to various independent power com-

209

panies. The suit came to trial at St. Louis in June of 1886. Greatly to everyone's surprise, the presiding federal judge disallowed the priority of Edison's lamp patents on technical grounds. Of course, Edison Electric Light immediately appealed to a higher court. But now the matter was in the hands of the lawyers, and Edison's gloomy predictions were confirmed as the preliminary skirmishes began to drag on for months and years. It would be three years before the trial resumed, and three more years before a final decision was handed down. In that time, Edison's patents remained in doubt, and the competitors felt free to ignore his claims.

Patent troubles aside, the revitalized company did well under the Johnson regime. Pearl Street had long since reached full capacity, and Edison Electric Light in Eaton's presidency had refused to let its operating subsidiary, Edison Illuminating, expand its generating facilities. At Johnson's orders the First District received a supplementary power station at 60 Liberty Street in 1886, and work began on stations in two new districts. These stations, one at West 39th Street and one at West 26th Street, were opened in 1888. One measure of the lack of progress under Eaton is the roster of Edison Illuminating customers. After the quick early growth to 513 customers in 1883, most new lighting business was simply turned away, so that on December 31, 1888, the company was serving only 710 accounts. A year later, though, it recorded 1,213 customers, and by 1899 had passed the 10,000 mark. (Consolidated Edison had 3,042,000 electric meters on its lines at the end of 1965, and its revenue from electric service was $693,591,000.)

The growth of Edison Illuminating and other electric utilities meant increased business for Edison's manufacturing companies, since all the Edison utilities were bound by contract to use only Edison equipment and appliances. These businesses, Edison's chief sources of personal income, prospered in 1885. Edison Lamp Company, which had been such a woeful cash drain when organized, turned out 139,000 bulbs in 1885 and sold them at a net profit of ten cents apiece. Edison owned an 80 per cent interest in this company. The Edison Machine Works at Goerck Street now employed eight hundred workers; Bergmann & Co. had also expanded rapidly.

The long tension of his struggle had left Edison moody and easily discouraged, and even a small setback was enough to make him brood. Thus when the patent suit ran into trouble in mid-1886 and it seemed that the infringers would engulf his business, he said to Insull, "I do not know how we are going to live. I think I could go back and earn my living as a telegraph operator. Do you think, Sammy, that you could go back to earn your living as a stenographer?"

His pessimism was needless. Despite the competition, the Edison companies thrived. By October 1, 1886, there were five hundred isolated Edison plants in service in the United States and fifty-eight central stations. The grand foyer of the La Scala Opera House in Milan was brightened by Edison lighting, as was the Dom Pedro railway station in Rio de Janeiro, and the Variety Theater in Santiago, Chile. Edison incandescent lighting had reached Russia, South Africa, Germany, and a dozen other countries. The combined assets of the various Edison companies approached ten million dollars. Edison himself had quickly grown wealthy on dividends, royalties, and the profits of his manufacturing companies, and the tide of income steadily rose as a new boom in electric streetcars late in 1886 vastly increased the power load of the Edison stations. He had come through the time of debt and troubles, and found himself the proprietor of a great new industry. It seemed to many that the famed inventor—now thirty-nine years old and becoming portly —would quit the laboratory forever and settle down to a career as the nation's electrical tycoon. But that was not to be.

Lonely, vexed by the problem of raising three motherless children, he emerged from isolation within six months after his

211

wife's death and let himself be thrust into polite society. His friends shepherded him through dinners and drawing rooms, cast pretty girls in his way, and eventually arranged for him to meet eighteen-year-old Mina L. Miller, a girl of charm and attainment, the daughter of a successful Ohio industrialist. She captivated him at once and an engagement followed. Too deaf for ordinary conversation, Edison taught Morse code to young Mina, and sent messages of affection to her by tapping out his words in code on her hands. He proposed to her in this way.

On September 30, 1885, Edison made formal application by mail to Mina's father for her hand. "I trust you will not accuse me of egotism," he wrote, "when I say that my life and history and standing are so well known as to call for no statement concerning myself. My reputation is so far made that I recognize I must be judged by it for good or ill. . . ."

That winter, while the wedding plans proceeded, Edison purchased a country estate for his bride in keeping with his present position in life. A shadowy New York businessman had recently built a twenty-three room mansion called "Glenmont" on thirteen and one-half acres in Llewellyn Park, a private residential community within West Orange, New Jersey. Erected at a cost of some two hundred thousand dollars, Glenmont was a sumptuous home in the highest late-Victorian style. From the outside, the building of brick and red-painted clapboard seemed a confused hodgepodge of gables and balconies, but its interior was an elegant thing of oaken doors, mahogany staircases, and stained-glass windows. Its owner had run into financial difficulties and had absconded to Europe; his creditors put the place on sale, furnishings and all, at a fourth of the original cost.

An earlier Edison might have scorned such ostentation as this mansion. But Edison felt that he must now live on the grand scale, and that Mina deserved the most magnificent surroundings he could give her. Glenmont became his. Today it is part of the Edison National Historic Site, under Federal ownership, and we can see it as the Edison family knew it. Lovely gardens surround the house. The library on the ground floor is adorned with rows of books in fine leather bindings: Dickens, Scott, Wilkinson's *Ancient Egyptians*, Gibbon, Dumas, Layard's *Nineveh and Babylon*. They seem to have been chosen for their decorative value, for few appear to have been read. Upstairs, in the large family den, are more books, these in humble cloth binding and well thumbed by Edison: Poe, Balzac, Hawthorne, and such forgotten detective-story writers as Gaboriau. The furniture of the house is of the highest quality, and the lighting —incandescent, of course—is subdued.

Half a mile from this shrine of status and power Edison built his new laboratories, on a scale to dwarf the abandoned establishment at Menlo Park. Edison jotted in his notebook,

> I will have the best equipped & largest Laboratory extant, and the facilities incomparably superior to any other *for rapid & cheap development of an invention* & working it up into Commercial shape with models patterns & special machinery. In fact there is no similar institution in Existence. . . . Inventions that formerly took months & cost large sums can now be done 2 or 3 days with very small expense, as I shall carry a stock of almost every conceivable material.

The Edison laboratory on Main Street in West Orange has been part of the Edison National Historic Site since 1956, and has been preserved as it was on the day of Edison's death in 1931. Visitors today can see how well Edison carried out his own intentions for the laboratory. It consists of five brick buildings arranged in a quadrangle and surrounded by a fence. The main building, a three story structure some two hundred fifty feet long, contains machine shops, an engine room, stockrooms, a glass-blowing room, and a splendid library of technical books housed in a three-tiered room thirty feet high. The long, narrow, dark main stockroom has thousands of small drawers that hold every conceivable raw material: resins, gums, feathers, teeth, bones, deer horns, tortoise shell, elephant hide, peacocks' tails, amber, meerschaum, hoofs, macaroni, varnish and oils, chemicals beyond number, every kind of screw made, every kind of needle, rope, wire, twine, cord, human and animal hair, diamonds in folds of tissue paper, sharks' teeth, cocoons, silk, ostrich plumes, and a good deal more. If Edison needed a substance for an experiment, he wanted to have it on the spot.

The other four buildings are smaller, and lie at right angles to the main building. The first, once Edison's physics laboratory, is now a museum housing early phonographs and dynamos. The second, the chemical laboratory, still contains the dried goldenrod from which Edison was attempting to extract rubber in his last days. The third building was a storage shed, and the fourth, the metallurgical laboratory. Edison gathered about him a staff of some fifty men, ranging from laborers and mechanics to physicists and chemists. Yet somehow the imposing West Orange laboratory never equalled the Menlo Park place in excitement or productivity.

Edison was married to Mina at her family home in Akron on February 24, 1886. The couple vanished for a Florida honeymoon on which Edison remained wholly incommunicado, and took up housekeeping at their New Jersey villa in April. His troubled years seemed to be behind him, and fame, fortune, and domestic bliss would surely be his lot in the days to come.

thirteen

Edison
General
Electric

THE boom year of 1886 saw Edison's manufacturing companies receiving more business than they could easily handle. Edison was still liberal in advancing credit to the young electric utilities, but the New York bankers were not equally liberal in extending credit to him. At one point in 1886 he found himself with orders on hand needing $200,000 in copper, and no cash with which to buy it. Money was tight. To enhance his meager working capital Edison had borrowed against his stock holdings until he could borrow no more. The bankers were willing to accept stock in Edison Electric Light as collateral, but they took a cooler attitude toward the shares of unknown power companies in Idaho and Oregon on which Edison tried to raise cash.

In one fashion and another Edison juggled his way through the money squeeze, thanks largely to the cleverness of Insull. Insull had a fundamental abhorrence for buying on cash. "Never pay cash when you can give a note," he said, "and then meet your notes promptly. That's the way to establish your credit." It was a rule he followed strictly in his own later business endeavors, until the dark day in 1932 when he could no longer meet his notes and was crushed by the New York bankers.

The little factories in downtown New York were inadequate for the great volume of Edison's 1886 business. Early that year he began looking for a new location. He sent scouts across New Jersey, Pennsylvania, and upstate New York. Harry Livor, the Edison agent who was touring the Mohawk Valley, arrived that spring in the sleepy town of Schenectady, New York. Its population then was fourteen thousand, and it had just one major employer, the Schenectady Locomotive Works, known locally as "the big shop."

Walter McQueen, the plant superintendent of "the big shop," had quarreled with the company's president in 1885 and had withdrawn to set up a competitive firm. He borrowed some money and started to put up two factory buildings for what would be the McQueen Locomotive Works, on a broad expanse of level ground west of town along the Mohawk. The buildings were still roofless late in 1885 when McQueen's backer died and the company foundered. When Livor came to town some months later, he learned that the site and the unfinished factories were up for sale.

Livor liked the site and summoned Edison, who journeyed to Schenectady to pass judgment on it. Edison was pleased— until he heard that the asking price was $45,000. Edison offered $37,500 and refused to go higher. There the matter hung fire a while, but the Schenectady Chamber of Commerce, shrewdly realizing that it was foolish to let a few thousand dollars stand in the way of bringing such a huge employer to town, convassed the leading merchants and raised the difference of $7,500. The owners of the property got their price, and Edison got his factory buildings. Shortly the Electric Tube Company, one of the least profitable and most space-consuming of Edison's companies, was shifted to Schenectady. The Edison Shafting Company, another minor subsidiary, soon followed it.

There was no immediate plan to move the Edison Machine Works out of New York City, but labor troubles forced Edison's hand. He had never been very sympathetic to the demands of labor in the abstract, though he looked after individual workmen in a tender, paternalistic way. Early in the existence of the Edison Lamp Company, eighty of his skilled lamp assemblers had formed a union and attempted to dictate working conditions. Edison promptly invented a labor-saving assembling machine, put it into use, and fired the dissident men. The union collapsed.

He took similarly drastic action when the Goerck Street workmen grew unruly in the summer of 1886. As he related to one of his biographers,

> It seems I had rather a socialistic strain in me; and I raised the pay of the workmen twenty-five cents [a day]. . . . But the men thought they would try coercion and get a little more, as we were considered easy marks. Whereupon they struck at a time that was critical. However we were short of money for payroll, and we concluded . . . it would give us a couple of weeks to catch up. So when the men went out they appointed a committee to meet us; but for two weeks they could not find us. Finally they said they would like to go back. We said all right. . . . When they went back to the Goerck Street shops they found them empty of machinery. It was quite a novelty to the men not to be able to find us when they wanted to, and they didn't relish it at all.

Edison had quietly transferred the Machine Works to Schenectady. On July 30, 1886 it absorbed the Tube Company and the Shafting Company in the interests of simplified corporate structure, and now all generating and transmitting equipment was to be manufactured at one location. (The Lamp Company, with hundreds of employees, remained at Harrison, New Jersey, and Bergmann & Co. stayed in New York City.) Charles Batchelor and John Kruesi, who had shared the administrative responsibilities at Goerck Street, moved to Schenectady to run the combined operation.

The factory expanded beyond all the dreams of the Chamber

of Commerce. New buildings went up at once. On August 25, 1888, *Electrical World* published an article called, "A Day with Edison at Schenectady," which praised the Edison plant as "one of the greatest exemplifications of the power of American inventive genius, and . . . an establishment where, from beginning to end, a new art is illustrated by new processes." The author was T. Commerford Martin, later to be one of Edison's biographers. Martin told of "a vast establishment of noble machine shops" where "the prosaic and the marvelous jostle each other." At that time there were twenty-six separate buildings, employing about eight hundred men; today the Schenectady plant of what has become the General Electric Company has a main street a mile long. "Here," wrote Martin, "are six thousand feet of shafting and some fifty thousand feet of belting, driving nearly four hundred separate mechanisms in the production of apparatus whose birth was yesterday."

The Edison idea was invading the entire nation. In December of 1886 the Edison Electric Light Company of Philadelphia was organized, with a capital of $1,000,000, and Professor William D. Marks of the University of Pennsylvania was hired at a salary of $4500 a year to be its supervising engineer. Professor Marks designed a plan for a central power station so revolutionary that it baffled the parent company in New York, whose approval was needed. Edison himself was called in for an opinion and, after some study, announced that Mark's designs were better than his own and would increase profits by a third. They called for a massive eight-story power plant with fourteen 500-horsepower Armington-Sims steam engines and twenty-eight 3,000-lamp dynamos; Marks clearly saw that operating efficiency depended on expanding the output of each plant. The station went into service on March 5, 1889, serving 25,000 lights. Within six years Philadelphia Edison's plant, then the largest in the world, had quadrupled its output.

In Brooklyn, arc light companies had gone into service in

1885, but they had feared to trespass on the Edison incandescent patents. That left the way clear for the founding of Edison Electric Illuminating Company of Brooklyn in March, 1887. A month later it negotiated a licensing arrangement with Edison Electric Light and began to build its power plant— located, by a happy coincidence, at 358-362 Pearl Street, Brooklyn. Its operations commenced in 1889. Much of its early income came from Brooklyn's new electric trolley cars; by 1892 Brooklynites (and their baseball team) were being called "Trolley Dodgers" as the lively cars shot through the streets.

The Edison Electric Illuminating Company of Boston was incorporated in January, 1886. Edison Illuminating Company of Michigan was founded three months later to serve Detroit. Dozens of others followed. Insull invented the Association of Edison Illuminating Companies as a trade organization for the exchange of ideas and practical experiences. Edison, who had accepted securities in part payment of equipment bills, owned stock interests in scores of the new power companies. He tried to sell these securities to finance his own business, but found no ready market for them. Willy-nilly he thus began building up a portfolio of utility stocks, chiefly in small, insecure companies. He knew there was great potential value in these stocks—which had a nominal par value of millions of dollars—but at the moment the involuntary portfolio merely complicated his already complex financial position.

In the midst of the exciting expansion of the electrical industry, Edison returned to a discarded invention of the previous decade: the phonograph. It had remained a toy since he had set it aside in 1878, nearly forgotten by those who had hailed it so rapturously then. But in 1885 Chichester Bell, the cousin of Alexander Graham Bell, had turned his attention to it, developing a machine he called a "graphophone" which was not too different from the Edison phonograph. It differed enough, though, so that Bell was able to get a patent on his recording process in May, 1886. Then Bell and a partner privately approached Edison to suggest joint exploitation of the new machine. They said that they recognized Edison as the real inventor of the "talking machine," admitting that their own work was merely a refinement of his ideas. They would put up the capital and turn over their patents, and Edison would handle the production and promotion, on a fifty-fifty basis.

Edison angrily refused. He called them "pirates" and would enter into no partnerships. Stung by their offer, he resolved to perfect his own abandoned device and seize the phonograph market. Perhaps it was an unreasonable response, marking the testiness that had crept into his character since the death of his first wife, but it served to get him back into the laboratory after three years of manufacturing distractions. Placing Insull virtually in control of the electrical business, Edison returned to the drawing boards.

Though hampered by his deafness, he rapidly produced striking improvements in the 1878 phonograph. Six months of hard work in 1887 left him confident enough to announce that he had never actually abandoned his "favorite invention" and would soon be in commercial production. He worked with his right ear—in which he still had a degree of hearing—pressed against the revamped instruments, sometimes even biting into the playback horn to carry the sound vibrations through the bones of his head to his auditory nerve. Select financiers, none of them connected with Edison Electric Light, were invited to West Orange early in 1888 to examine the new phonograph as a possible investment.

Meanwhile Bell had sold his graphophone patent to another manufacturer, who hastily got some machines on the market. Edison claimed patent infringement and hurried to make his own phonograph ready for sale. His efforts were as strenuous as any he had made in the Menlo Park days. A famous photograph, taken "as he appeared at 5 A.M. on June 16, 1888, after five days without sleep," showed the inventor slouched bleakly before his phonograph, head propped against his hand as he listened through earphones to the instrument. Not even the birth of Mina Edison's first child, on May 31, 1888, had long interrupted the breathless pace of work. He produced his machine at last, and it was superior to Bell's. The manufacturer who had bought the Bell patent suggested a consolidation; Edison accepted and licensed the other man's North American Phonograph Company to market the talking machine. Thousands were sold, and copies of the "five days without sleep" picture were distributed as advertising matter, helping to spread the legend of Edison's superhuman endurance. By 1893 North American Phonograph had collapsed in a business depression, and Edison, as principal creditor and now chief stockholder, took the business over himself. For the next thirty-five years his Edison Phonograph Company would be the leader in the sale of phonographs as well as an important manufacturer of phonograph records.

In 1888, the year of the perfected phonograph, Edison found time to patent a new incandescent lamp whose filament consisted not of carbonized bamboo but of molded and "squirted" cellulose; he also worked on a new type of mining machinery and began preliminary studies of what would materialize as the motion picture. In his spare time he functioned as a spokesman for electricity, still trying to give the public some inkling of what the enigmatic new force was all about. When James Gordon Bennett of the *Herald* forwarded a reader's question about electricity to Edison in August, 1888, the inventor replied:

> This gentlemen asks where all the electric power comes from that runs our modern electric lights. The Herald can easily ascertain this by sending a reporter downstairs in their electric light department to interview the coal pile—

The sun shining several thousand years ago on rank vegetation stored up the energy which lights the NYork Herald. . . .

1888, in addition, was the year of consolidation for Edison's scattered electrical companies. Some sort of reorganization was necessary; their growth had been too disorderly, and they were in need of an infusion of fresh working capital. Through previous consolidations, only three manufacturing companies remained: the Lamp Company, the Machine Works, and Bergmann & Co. A fourth firm, Sprague Electric Railway and Motor Company, had come into being in 1884 to manufacture heavy equipment not already produced by Edison. Edison had no investment in the company himself, and was not overly happy about its existence, but it was run by Edison men like Frank Sprague and Edward Johnson and was partly owned by Edison Electric Light, thus giving it an odd semi-independent status within the Edison group. Above these four manufacturing concerns was the original corporation of 1878, Edison Electric Light, which controlled all the Edison electrical patents but otherwise had come to play something of a parasitic role.

Back into this jumbled picture, early in 1888, came the German promoter Henry Villard. Villard, an early Edison supporter, had been wiped out in the financial panic of 1883-84. After losing his railroad empire he had returned to Germany, where he became the agent of a powerful financial group that looked to control the electrical industry throughout the world. Among Villard's backers were several banks, a large German electrical equipment company, and several private capitalists. This group saw a grand consolidation of the Edison interests as a first step toward the formation of an international German-controlled electrical cartel.

Villard came forward with a plan to combine Edison's three manufacturing companies, the parent holding company, and the tottering Sprague Electric Railway and Motor Company into one corporation, thus sweeping together the Edison and Morgan groups that had grown so far apart. Morgan was willing, so long as he got a good price. Edison was willing, too. His electrical shops had always been undercapitalized, involving him and Insull in an endless search for operating funds. Now that some three thousand workers were on the payroll, the strain of finding cash was becoming unbearable, even though the three companies had total sales of nearly $7,000,000 a year and a combined annual profit of $700,000. Bankruptcy was an ever-present threat, an absurd situation for such prospering firms, but they were so loaded down with the dubious utility stocks accepted in lieu of cash that they were eternally hard put to meet their bills. Here was a way out.

Villard's terms were generous, as they had to be in order to gain control of companies that had been nurtured so tenderly by Bergmann, Upton, Batchelor, and Edison's other partners, through years of difficulty into a time of relative success. For the three manufacturing companies Villard offered $1,100,000 in cash and $2,100,000 (at par value) in the stock of the new consolidated corporation. The offer for the Sprague company and three tiny satellites was $950,000 in stock. Morgan and his associates held $1,500,000 in stock of Edison Electric Light, for which they had paid only $779,600; Villard offered to exchange for it $2,625,000 in the new stock at par value, plus $1,375,000 in trust certificates ultimately convertible into common stock of the new corporation. Finally, $2,250,000 worth of stock in the new corporation would be purchased by Villard's German backers at a cost of $1,750,000 in cash. Of this money, $1,100,000 would be turned over to the former owners of the three Edison manufacturing companies as the agreed-upon cash part of the purchase price, and the remaining $650,000 would become the working capital of the consolidated company. As an extra sweetener, Edison would be given $500,000 of stock in the new company as advance payment for his future inventive services.

Edison found these terms quite acceptable. He would come away with a lavish cash payment and millions of dollars' worth of stock in a powerful new company, and he would be freed from his nagging day-by-day financial problems. However, Morgan balked. He felt too much was going to Edison and not enough to the stockholders of Edison Electric Light. He insisted that his group be given $3,500,000 in new stock for its interest. This was a piratical demand, for it would yield the Morgan group a 40 per cent slice of the new company in exchange for two sets of uncertain assets: Edison's patent rights, and the securities of various power companies which the parent holding company had unavoidably accumulated as royalty payments. The Edison patents were now under heavy attack in court, and the most important of them were due to expire in a few more years anyway. As for the utility stock, no one could say what value it had.

But Morgan had his way—and also succeeded in lopping off the proposed gift of $500,000 in stock to Edison. The revised offer still amounted to an attractive deal for the Edison group: $2,158,333 in stock and $1,666,667 in cash for control of the three companies. Edison conferred with Insull. "Mr. Insull and I were afraid," he later wrote, "that we might get into trouble for lack of money. Therefore . . . we concluded it was better to be sure than to be sorry." They accepted the terms set down by Villard and Morgan.

In January of 1889 the merger was consummated. Edison Lamp Company, Edison Machine Works, Bergmann & Co., and Sprague Electric Railway were consolidated with the parent Edison Electric Light to form the new Edison General Electric Company. Also included in the merger were the Canadian Edison Manufacturing Company, a recently formed subsidiary, and the Edison United Manufacturing Company, a sales outlet. The Edison Construction Department had previously been incorporated into Edison's other companies.

No power utilities became part of Edison General Electric. Edison Illuminating, which had been a subsidiary of Edison Electric Light, was now an independent concern. However, Edison General Electric owned a large stock interest in the New York utility, and also many of the Edison G.E. stockholders held shares in Edison Illuminating. The securities of other power companies that had been accepted by Edison and the Electric Light Company in the past now went into the portfolio of Edison General Electric.

The consolidation seemed to benefit every party involved. The Germans and Villard had their first leg toward a giant cartel. The Morgan group had come away with $3,500,000 of valuable stock in return for its $779,600 investment in the original Edison Electric Light. Edison and his partners were made rich men. Edison himself received $1,750,000 in cash and stocks. Sigmund Bergmann, whose share was a million dollars, went to Germany and founded a large electrical concern there. Edward Johnson retired to the luxury of a Connecticut estate. Even young Insull's share was $75,000.

There were important psychological advantages for Edison, too. He had escaped from the conservatism of the parent holding company. Shortly before the consolidation went through, he had written to Villard to complain, "With the leaden collar of the Edison Electric Light Co. around me, I have never been able to show what can be done. . . . Let me break the leaden collar and you will see a brainy competition that will show them [Thomson-Houston and other patent infringers] what real competition is." Now he was free of that "leaden collar," and free also of financial worries. In 1890 he told Villard, "I have been under a desperate strain for money for 22 years, and when I sold out, one of the greatest inducements was the sum of cash received, so as to free my mind from financial stress, and thus enable me to go ahead in the technical field."

On the other hand, he had been induced to surrender his

control over the industry he had created. Each year there had been a progressive weakening of Edison's investment in electric light and power. Now he had virtually ceased to be an owner at all. His once-dominant stake in Edison Electric Light had long since disappeared. He had surrendered his potentially valuable bundle of power-company securities as part of the consolidation deal. He had ceased to have an active interest in Edison Electric Illuminating of New York. All that remained to him was a 10 per cent share in Edison General Electric—worth a fortune, of course, but not entitling him to any real say in the company's affairs.

He had a place on the Edison G.E. board of directors, along with three of his men, Upton, Batchelor, and Insull. But Villard and Morgan's men held five of the nine places on the board, and ran the show. Soon Edison rarely bothered to attend the board meetings.

Insull, as second vice-president of the new company, had full charge of its manufacturing and sales activities. For the first time this remarkable if overambitious man had sufficient working capital to bring his ideas to fruition, and he began a sweeping reorganization and reorientation. Insull's goals were to cut fixed costs by diversifying operations and keeping the plant busy at all times; to cut prices through increased efficiency, thus achieving greater sales volume and profits; and to expand by borrowing, by raising new capital, and by plowing earnings back into the business. In a way, Insull was one of the first of the modern corporate managers.

He divided the country into seven sales districts and set up active branch offices. He eliminated wasteful overlapping between the merged companies. He abolished the easy-going policy of taking payment in stock from the local power companies who were Edison General Electric's chief customers. As the 1891 annual report declared, "The General Company could have done a much larger business if it had been willing to accept

226

securities in payment for orders; but . . . a strict rule was adopted of declining all such and doing business exclusively on a cash or short credit basis."

The results were impressive. Orders poured in and were swiftly executed. Philadelphia Edison's huge power plant was such a success that Edison Illuminating of New York had Edison G.E. build an even bigger one. By 1890 the Edison power companies around the country were serving 1,300,000 incandescent lamps.

Profits were rising both for the big manufacturing company and for the scores of Edison power companies. All tried to follow the Insull gospel of cutting prices to gain greater profits through higher volume. In New York, Edison Illuminating made the first cuts in its rate schedule since its founding in 1882. It had been charging 1.2 cents per 16-candlepower lamp-hour at Pearl Street, and 1.1 cents uptown. In 1890 it substituted the new unit of the kilowatt-hour, and posted a rate of 20 cents a kilowatt-hour, which worked out to a good-sized reduction in costs. (Consolidated Edison's basic rate today is less than 4 cents a kilowatt-hour.)

In Philadelphia, Professor William Marks cut Edison rates from 1.125 cents per lamp-hour to .75 cents as a promotional move. There was an immediate and profitable increase in business. But Marks failed to see the significance of his own move and toyed with the thought of raising rates to 1 cent per lamp-hour, which brought this Insull-inspired letter from Edison on April 7, 1891:

> To my mind the raising of the price from ¾ to 1¢ per lamp hour is a bid for competition. I am a believer in *Insuring the permanency of an investment* by keeping prices so low that there is no inducement to others to come in and ruin it. There seems to be a law in commercial things as in nature. If one attempts to obtain more profit than general average he is immediately punished by competitions.

Insull's radical belief in profit through price reduction has become an article of faith for nearly every electric utility in the country. The average price per kilowatt-hour has dropped from 20 cents at the time of Edison General Electric's founding to 9.1 cents in 1912, 7 cents in 1926, 5.01 cents in 1935, 3.22 cents in 1946, and less than 2.4 cents in the 1960's. At the same time, revenues, profits, and dividends have showed steady climbs.

Despite the feverish brilliance of Insull, Edison General Electric had its problems: Insull opposed taking utility stock as payment; Villard enthusiastically favored the idea. This created a powerful inner conflict. Villard saw Edison G.E. as evolving eventually into a holding company that not only manufactured electrical equipment but that controlled all the utilities selling power to consumers, so he advocated accepting common stock from the power companies whenever possible. Though Insull usually had his way in this debate, it undermined the stability of the corporation's board of directors.

Much more serious was the company's technical shortcoming. It lacked engineering talent. The world's most famous inventor was supposedly the "brain" of the company, but Edison had lost interest in the electrical arts. He had worked out the system; he had seen it into practical use; now, his creative urges satisfied, he had no more to offer in this field.

It happened that Edison G.E.'s rivals were simmering with bold new technological ideas. In the old days, Edison would have met such a challenge with a torrent of wonders, but now he refused even to believe that a challenge existed. Though only in his early forties, he emerged in the odd position of the arch-conservative, the defender of the status quo. He became the stubborn, reactionary old man of the electrical industry. His stubbornness led to the downfall of Edison General Electric and to his own final departure from the industry that was his personal creation.

fourteen

Alternating
Currents

THE existence of two types of electric current had been known since the dawn of the electrical age. Hippolyte Pixii's generator of 1832 had had a rotating magnetic field that cut the conductors first in one direction and then in the other. This produced a series of interrupted electrical pulses as the magnets swung back and forth; the flow of electricity reached a maximum in one direction, then decreased, moved toward a maximum in the other direction, and reversed again to begin a new cycle.

Such an "alternating" current did not seem useful to the early experimenters. Ampère had suggested a simple device called a commutator, which converted the oscillating or alternating current into a non-pulsating "direct" current, and commutators became standard features on the dynamos of the arc light era.

Edison's first generating machines were direct-current dynamos, but his early commitment to d.c. was accidental, to a large extent. For the purpose of providing incandescent lighting, it did not matter whether Edison used d.c. or a.c. The dynamo technology of 1878 was almost exclusively a d.c. technology, and so he chose to make no departure from it. Before long, though,

229

he was irrevocably wedded to the d.c. concept as an essential part of his system.

What was important to Edison as he created his system was not the type of current he used, but the voltage. The Edison system was based on power that traveled at 110 volts all the way from the generating station to the consumer. The great advantage of this was its safety. Current at 110 volts and at the low amperage sufficient for electric lighting could do no harm; a customer who came in contact with an unshielded line would receive a mild shock, no more. The danger of fire was low, too. Sensitive to the problems inherent in getting a new kind of illumination across to a suspicious public, Edison wished to avoid any possibility of spectacular electrical disasters, so he opted for the safest form of distribution.

However, low voltages had a built-in drawback: they limited the distance of transmission. Current moving with such a modest force could be carried no more than a mile or two from the generating station; then the drop in voltage became so great that the outlying lights dimmed. In addition, much of the power would be dissipated in the form of heat. Under Edison's low-voltage transmission system, Edison's own great concept of the central station was seriously impaired, for 110-volt service required a chain of power stations at close intervals in order to supply any large city with electricity. At best an Edison station could serve some sixteen square miles.

Ideally, the solution was to have power leave the generating station at a high voltage, and then to step it down to a safe 110 volts before it reached the customer. But this was technically impossible on the Edison system. The young Edison would have looked for some way to *make* it possible; the middle-aged Edison simply accepted the situation as a regrettable innate flaw in his design, and left it at that.

But there was a way—with alternating current.

The germ of the long-distance a.c. transmission system lay in the original work of Faraday. His first successful experiment had made use of two coils wound on an iron core; by stopping or starting a current in one coil, he induced a current in the other. Although he did not realize it, the basis of the transformer, or voltage-changer, could be found in this experiment.

Seven years later, in 1838, the American Joseph Henry used Faraday's two-coil arrangement as a step-down transformer. One coil consisted of many turns of wire, the other of only a few; high-voltage power entered the first coil, and was stepped down to a low voltage in the second.

The transformer received little further attention until 1882, when Lucien Gaulard of France and John D. Gibbs of England produced a transformer specifically designed to reduce the voltage of a.c. power en route from the generator to the consumer. Gaulard and Gibbs obtained an English patent on their work in 1883, but in practice it had serious mechanical defects and could not be used without modification.

The modifications were quick in coming. In 1885 three Hungarian inventors found a way to employ the Gaulard-Gibbs transformer in long-distance power installations. Their device, called the "Z.B.D. transformer" after the initials of its inventors, went into immediate use in Europe. It permitted power first to be boosted to very high voltage as it left the generator, then to be stepped down again as it reached the consumer—with remarkably little energy loss over great distances. The higher the voltage used in transmission, the less the loss on the line.

Rights to the Z.B.D. system were offered to Edison in 1886. He sent Upton to Europe to inspect the equipment, and at Upton's suggestion Edison paid $5000 for a three-year option, against a total price of $20,000. But Edison could not bring himself to veer from his low-voltage d.c. transmission system. In November, 1886 he received a report from a Berlin engineering firm to the effect that the Z.B.D. system was troublesome, costly to install, and dangerous to work with. That was all Edison needed to hear. He allowed the option to lapse, and angrily rejected the suggestions of his associates that he give the Hun-

231

garian transformer a further trial. Edison's adherence to his own original system had become something deeply personal, a matter for the emotions, not the reason. He clung to his 110-volt concept despite all advice to the contrary.

Yet younger men all over Europe and America were excited by the new development. High-voltage transmission suddenly was the technological darling of the moment. Of course, it would require a changeover from d.c. to a.c. power. Since transformers functioned only with a changing current, the output of d.c. generators could be neither stepped up nor stepped down with transformers. High voltages required the use of a.c. equipment. And that produced certain new problems. Alternating current could not be used for driving electric motors; it seemed to demand two or three times as much coal per kilowatt hour as direct current; and it rendered obsolete most of the existing capital plant of the power industry. Nevertheless, the forward-looking men of that industry were confident that someone would invent a feasible a.c. electric motor and that the generating cost of a.c. could be made comparable to that of d.c. As for the obsolescence of existing equipment, that would cease to matter in time. Alternating current was sure to win universal acceptance.

Edison—nearly alone—fought the new trend.

His option on the Z.B.D. patents gave him the exclusive right to use the new transformer in the United States until 1889. Since that was the case, rival manufacturers had no choice but to go back to the defective Gaulard-Gibbs device and attempt to modify it themselves in a way that circumvented the Hungarians. The most eager of these rivals was George Westinghouse of Pittsburgh, who had gone into the electric business in 1885.

Westinghouse, one year Edison's senior, had founded his industrial fortunes on his invention of the air brake for railways. Bold, ambitious, even reckless, he dreamed of an electrical empire to rival Edison's, and by liberal use of cash had attracted some of the best engineers of the day away from the ever more conservative Edison organization.

The new Westinghouse Electrical & Manufacturing Company sought to steal a march on Edison by getting control of that segment of the electrical field that Edison scorned: high-voltage alternating current equipment of 1,000 volts or more. For that Westinghouse needed a practicable transformer.

Westinghouse bought the American rights to the Gaulard-Gibbs transformer and assigned the job of making it work properly to a young engineering consultant, William A. Stanley. The flaw in the Gaulard-Gibbs system was that it employed a number of transformers to be connected in series, so that they could not work independently. Stanley found a patentable way of connecting transformers in parallel and making each transformer automatically regulate itself, thus permitting independent control. On March 6, 1886, the first commercial alternating-current lighting system went into operation in Great Barrington, Massachusetts, using the Stanley transformers. At Great Barrington Stanley generated power at 500 volts just outside town, stepped it up to 3000 volts for transmission, then lowered it to 500 volts again for use in lighting. The transmission distance was only 4000 feet, but the principle was established; Westinghouse saw no reason why the Stanley system could not be used to send power cheaply for distances of many miles.

Westinghouse, in 1886, also purchased the United States Electric Lighting Company, which had control of the contested Maxim incandescent lamp patents. Now he proposed to compete in both spheres of the electrical industry. Through Westinghouse Electric he would manufacture high-voltage equipment; through United States Electric he would set up power companies that, by taking advantage of the economies of long-distance transmission, would outstrip the Edison companies. Where he could, Westinghouse would rely on the non-Edison technology of a.c. Where he could not, he intended to invade the Edison patents, whose validity was under attack in the courts. In an advertisement exceptional for its blandly self-congratulatory tone Westinghouse declared:

> We regard it as fortunate that we have deferred entering the electrical field until the present moment. Having thus profited by the public experience of others, we enter ourselves for competition, hampered by a minimum of expense for experimental outlay. . . . In short, our organization is free, in large measure, of the load with which [other] electrical enterprises seem to be encumbered. The fruit of this . . . we propose to share with the customer.

That is, having allowed Edison to bear the burden of developing the electrical industry, Westinghouse planned to undersell him by making use of his pioneering work.

In March of 1887 Westinghouse began to move into New York City, Edison's home grounds, with an a.c. incandescent lighting system. He organized the Safety Electric Light and Power Company and licensed it to use the Westinghouse system of generation and distribution of electricity by alternating current. Safety Electric began to buy into an existing arc light company, United States Illuminating, which held several important street and park contracts. Soon Safety Electric controlled United States Illuminating; it changed its name in 1889 to United Electric Light and Power Company and began to spread the Westinghouse system into those parts of Manhattan that Edison Illuminating had not yet reached.

Naturally the older company fought back. In 1888 it denounced the Westinghouse system in a pamphlet that declared:

> They cannot make it safe.
> They cannot make it reliable.
> They cannot make it run twelve 16-candlepower lamps per horsepower.
> They cannot make its lamps even.

234

They cannot make its lamps last a reasonable time.
They cannot make it sell by meter.
They cannot make it run motors.

Some of these charges were true at the time; others, particularly the accusation of unsafeness, were not. But the men who had made such a deep financial and emotional investment in d.c. could not abide the thought that their system was obsolescent.

Edison himself, though no longer directly concerned with the fortunes of the Edison Illuminating Company, was seriously perturbed by the spread of a.c. It was an attack on his technical judgment, he felt; he was worried, also, about Westinghouse's talk of using power at 5,000 or even 10,000 volts. Contemporary insulating techniques did not seem adequate for such voltages, Edison felt. To Edward Johnson he wrote:

> Just as certain as death Westinghouse will kill a customer within 6 months after he puts in a system of any size. He has got a new thing and it will require a great deal of experimenting to get it working practically. It will never be free from danger. . . .
> None of his plans worry me in the least; only thing that disturbs me is that Westinghouse is a great man for flooding the country with agents and travelers. He is ubiquitous and will form numerous companies before we know anything about it.

Edison's earlier rival, Thomson-Houston Electric, was also toying with a.c. Elihu Thomson had constructed a rudimentary transformer in 1879, but he did nothing with it then because, like everyone else at the time, he was building d.c. dynamos. After the success of the three Hungarians provoked interest in a.c., Thomson hastily filed an application in November of 1885 for a patent on his transformer. But several other groups, among them the Gaulard-Gibbs team, contested the application and

Thomson's patent was not granted for nearly twenty years, only to be thrown out anyway on its first court test.

Patent or not, Thomson saw the advantages of a long-distance a.c. transmission system, and continued his research. By the spring of 1887 Thomson-Houston was manufacturing a.c. dynamos—"alternators," as they were called—and transformers. However, Thomson was perturbed by the supposed danger of bringing high-voltage lines to the consumers, and so Thomson-Houston held back from any really enthusiastic promotion of a.c. for several years, leaving a clear field to Westinghouse while it worked on protective devices.

The problem of the electric motor also hindered the spread of a.c. in 1887. All existing motors worked on d.c., and d.c. alone; no one yet knew a way of adapting them for a.c. use. Since the electrical industry was coming to depend for its revenues more and more on industrial power use, less and less on lighting, a practical a.c. motor was essential if the new system were to last.

Elihu Thomson built one of the first a.c. motors in May of 1887. It had a laminated magnet consisting of many disks of metal pressed together, and a laminated armature with three coils. The Thomson motor attracted considerable attention when it was displayed before a scientific group, but it did not go into production at once, and the aggressive Westinghouse gained a leading position with the a.c. motor of Nikola Tesla.

Tesla, a towering, mystical genius out of Yugoslavia, had once been part of the Edison organization but had slipped away. As an electrical inventor he was extraordinary, very likely superior in vision even to Edison. But he was a romantic, brooding figure of little practical awareness who could never have become a permanent part of the Edison research team. There was room in Edison's entourage for only one genius at a time; besides, Tesla believed passionately in the alternating current.

In 1882, in Budapest, Tesla was seized with a vision of an alternating-current motor: a rotating magnetic field that carried the armature around with it. The Tesla motor employed two alternating currents at once; the currents were equal in the frequency of their cycle of minimum-to-maximum amplitude, but were out of phase relative to each other. With one current or the other always at a maximum, the motor worked continuously. It was a brilliant idea, a landmark in engineering. But in 1882 there was no a.c. power source to drive Tesla's motor.

He drifted on to Paris soon after and took a job with the new Société Continentale Edison, the French Edison company. There he dutifully worked on d.c. lighting systems while inwardly pursuing his own dream. Early in 1883, sent to Strasbourg as a troubleshooter, he collected some spare parts and built the first working model of his motor, and a small dynamo to drive it. Everything worked as he had envisioned it. Tesla was then twenty-seven.

Calling some wealthy industrialists of Strasbourg together, he tried to interest them in forming a company to back him, for he knew that the Edison company had no desire even to hear about an a.c. system. But the Strasbourgers could not understand what Tesla was telling them, and he returned to Paris without the capital he had hoped to raise.

There he came to the attention of Charles Batchelor in the spring of 1884. Batchelor, sensing Tesla's brilliance, invited him to go to the United States and work directly with Edison. Naively confident that he could convert Edison to his own system, Tesla sank his savings into a steamship passage to New York. He arrived with four cents in cash, the clothes on his back, and the plans for his a.c. motor; he also carried a letter of introduction from Batchelor to Edison, saying, "I know two great men and you are one of them; the other is this young man."

Tesla went to Edison's Fifth Avenue office, presented his letter, and was treated to a discourse on the problems of Pearl Street. Edison would hear no talk of alternating current; he put Tesla to work at once on routine electrical work. When Tesla

237

solved a knotty problem with unexpected cleverness, Edison saw his merit and gave him harder assignments—without, however, raising his pay beyond that of a beginning technician. Feeling underpaid, and angered by Edison's refusal to consider his theories, Tesla came to the inevitable collision with his employer and resigned after a year. From the spring of 1886 to the spring of 1887 he supported himself as a day laborer, digging ditches and taking on occasional electrical jobs.

Then he found backers, and set up the Tesla Electric Company. Though their financial support was modest, Tesla was able to carry on his research and to apply for patents. Between November and December, 1887, Tesla filed for seven patents on his motor and on an electrical distribution system; so radically different were they from anything in existence that the applications were granted in only six months. Tesla was invited to explain his ideas at a meeting of the American Institute of Electrical Engineers on May 16, 1888. He had "arrived."

Now he held patents on a revolutionary power system. His high-voltage lines could carry power hundreds of miles with relatively little energy loss or voltage drop. His motors were far more efficient than the small d.c. motors then in use, and could handle much greater loads. But the Tesla Electric Company lacked the capital to make use of the patents. Inevitably, Tesla was summoned to meet George Westinghouse. Westinghouse offered the inventor a million dollars in cash for his patents, plus a generous royalty arrangement, and hired Tesla as a consultant.

Though the unpredictable Tesla soon quarreled with Westinghouse and returned to private research, his patents had passed into the manufacturer's control. Now it was Westinghouse, and not Edison, who held the technological advantage. Westinghouse could make use of the newest and most exciting ideas in the field; Edison, relegated to the role of grim defender of the past, was forced to rely on the great work of 1878-83 at a time when that work had passed into obsolescence. As often happens when a great man must occupy an untenable position, Edison grew more convinced that he was right each time Westinghouse added new proof that he was wrong. Thus began the famed "Battle of the Currents."

Edison set out to prove that a.c. was a menace to the public. He rigged an a.c. generator at West Orange that supplied current at 1,000 volts, and before invited audiences of reporters and other guests staged grisly demonstrations in which hapless dogs and cats were nudged out onto wired sheets of tin and electrocuted. The stray animals of upper New Jersey perished at a ghastly rate in this gruesome promotional campaign.

Then, in February of 1888, Edward Johnson issued a manifesto titled, "A Warning from the Edison Electric Light Company." It summarized the results of the animal executions and provided a long list of the fatalities caused by arc lights, which used high voltages. The pamphlet sideswiped Westinghouse and Thomson-Houston by branding them as "patent pirates" who were out to gain quick wealth by introducing a newfangled and risky kind of electricity to the American home.

Westinghouse issued relatively restrained denials, pointing out that the mishaps of arc light companies in 1880 had nothing to do with his own incandescent system of 1888, and that in any event high voltages would be used only in transmission lines; current entering the home would be stepped down to a voltage no greater than that favored by Edison.

Thomson-Houston stayed out of the battle. After its initial delay it had gone into full production of a.c. equipment, which Elihu Thomson at last regarded as perfectly safe. Thomson-Houston was selling hundreds of alternators and thousands of transformers now. As Elihu Thomson pointed out, a.c. was actually less deadly than d.c., given the same voltage and amperage. The only real danger in using a.c. lay in the possibility that a short-circuit in the transformer might allow a high voltage to emerge from the secondary, or step-down coil; but

Thomson found a means of protecting against this danger, and had no further fears of trouble. Nevertheless, Charles Coffin, the shrewd head of Thomson-Houston, preferred to let Westinghouse and Edison battle it out in the headlines while his company went ahead with steady output of the new equipment.

Edison's promotional campaign—sparked by the ingenuity of Samuel Insull—swung into a high level in the autumn of 1888. Edison lobbyists asked state legislatures for laws limiting electric circuits to 800 volts, and nearly succeeded in Ohio and Virginia. In New York, Edison took a different and much more bizarre approach: he persuaded the legislature to legalize the electric chair for the execution of condemned criminals—and saw to it that the fatal chair used Westinghouse equipment! What better way to dramatize the lethal nature of alternating current?

Harold P. Brown, a former laboratory assistant at West Orange, served as Edison's chief agent in this enterprise. Brown went before the legislators to preach the virtues of electrical execution—"instantaneous, painless, and humane"—and pushed through a bill, late in 1888, providing for the adoption of the electric chair in place of hanging. The New York State Legislature appointed Brown as a consultant to develop such a chair. With much fanfare he purchased three Westinghouse alternators and put on a display of their potency on March 2, 1889. The victims included several large dogs, four calves, and an elderly horse. Ten seconds at 800 volts finished off the dogs; the calves were bigger, and had greater resistance, but they died in fifteen seconds. The horse required twenty-five seconds at 1000 volts. For human beings, Brown recommended 2000 volts for rapid and painless dispatch.

A human being was available for this research: one William Kemmler, a condemned murderer. The state authorities were eager to try Mr. Edison's death chair, and so Kemmler was sentenced "to suffer death by electricity at Auburn Prison within the week beginning Monday, June 24, 1889."

Kemmler seemed pleased at the attention he would get and the place in history that would be his, but his lawyers objected. Hearings followed; objections were filed. Twice the prisoner was reprieved while more experiments were performed. At one hearing Edison was called to the witness stand to give his evidence. He was interrogated by Deputy Attorney General Poste, who asked, "What is your calling or profession?"

"Inventor," Edison replied.

"Have you devoted a great deal of attention to the subject of electricity?"

"Yes."

"How long have you been engaged in the work of an inventor or electrician?"

"Twenty-six years."

Edison was asked to explain the difference between continuous (direct) and alternating current. "A continuous current," he said, "is one that flows like water through a pipe. An alternating current is the same as if a body of water were allowed to flow through the pipe in one direction for a given time and then its direction reversed for a given time."

Had he measured the electrical resistance of human beings? Yes, he said, he had. Measurements of 250 people showed an average resistance of 1000 ohms, the highest being 1800, the lowest 600.

"In your judgment," Poste asked, "can an artificial electric current be generated and applied in such a manner as to produce death in human beings in every case?"

"Yes."

"Instantly?"

"Yes."

W. Bourke Cockran, one of Kemmler's lawyers, now cross-examined the inventor. Cockran was troubled by the point that different men had different resistances. What if Kemmler did not die at once, but met some hideous and lingering doom? "What would be the effect of the current on Kemmler in case

241

the current was applied for five or six minutes?" Cockran asked. "Would he not be carbonized?"

"No," Edison replied. "He would be mummified. All the water in his body would evaporate."

Edison expressed the belief that 1000 volts of one-ampere current would be ten times as much as was needed to kill any man with the Westinghouse alternator.

"That is your belief, not from knowledge?" Cockran asked.

"From belief," said Edison quietly. "I never killed anybody."

After lengthy debate, Kemmler's execution date was set for August 6, 1890. The warden of Auburn Prison was empowered to invite twenty-one witnesses. Most of the guests selected were scientific men, among them Edison—who, however, did not care to be present at Kemmler's death.

An ordinary commercial Westinghouse machine capable of producing a current at 1500 volts was used. It was driven by a steam engine in the prison basement; the power lines were run out of a window of the dynamo room to the roof of the jail and along the roof to the death chamber. A current varying in force from 800 to 1300 volts gave Kemmler his place in the annals of penology; the witnesses unofficially reported that the death had been slower and less pleasant than Edison had predicted.

None the less, electrocution became the rule in New York State, and Edison, at some loss in dignity, managed to frighten many Americans into thinking that a.c. was a public menace. Some of his own men, particularly Frank Sprague, pleaded with him to halt his campaign, but Edison had gone too far now to back down. All his prestige was pledged to direct current. Out of bitterness and testiness he had elevated his original short-sightedness to the status of an inflexible policy; it was the worst mistake of his career.*

---

* In later years Edison disliked speaking of the "Battle of the Currents." But in 1908 he encountered George Stanley, the son of the inventor of Westinghouse's transformer, and said to him, "By the way, tell your father I was wrong."

242

Through 1888 and 1889 it became increasingly apparent to most men in the field that the future of electricity lay with a.c. By the time William Kemmler went to his death in the summer of 1890, that fact seemed certain to virtually everyone but Edison. Among the converts to the new creed were the executives of Edison General Electric, although they did not dare suggest to Edison that he had outlived his usefulness in electrical engineering. A series of complicated developments grew out of Edison's vested interest in the outmoded system of electrical generation and transmission, and when the dust settled, Edison had been quietly shown to the exit.

fifteen

Mr. Edison
Frozen Out

WHEN Edison General Electric was formed out of a collection of smaller companies early in 1889, Edison felt a great pressure lifted from him. He was rich beyond any vulnerability now, and he had shifted his unwanted business burdens to other shoulders. Let Insull run the manufacturing company, let Villard dicker with the bankers, let the Edison G.E. lawyers prosecute the eternal patent suit against the competitors. He was going to relax.

In the summer of 1889 Edison and his wife planned a trip to Europe for the first vacation he had had in several years. The great Universal Exposition of 1889 at Paris was a veritable showplace of Edison wonders. A full acre of the fairgrounds was devoted to Edison's electric lights and phonographs, a third of all the space allotted to the United States in the fair's Temple of Machinery. Some three hundred cases of Edison equipment had been shipped to France earlier that year—the shipping costs alone were $2500—and a team of Edison men had been working for several months to get everything in order.

The first newspaper story of Edison's European tour appeared in the New York papers on April 27:

President Sadi-Carnot has been profuse in courtesies and attentions to Thomas Alva Edison, the American inventor, since the latter's arrival in Paris for the purpose of superintending the establishment of his exhibit of electrical apparatus on the Champs de Mars. Mr. Edison has been received at the official residence with the utmost cordiality by the President, and has had several interviews with him, in which M. Carnot has manifested the greatest interest in the inventor's work.

But a reporter from the New York *Evening Sun* had spoken only the day before to Edison's secretary at West Orange, and had been told that Edison was still at work in his laboratory. The reporter hurried down to West Orange and found Edison out— in New York, though, not in Paris. Batchelor appeared and said, when asked if Edison were in Paris, "All that I have got to say is that he was here this morning. If he is now in Paris he must have gone by the air-line." It developed that the "Edison" who had received such a warm greeting in France was an imposter.

The authentic Edison departed for Europe on August 3, 1889, with his twenty-two-year-old bride radiant beside him. He was greeted at the dock by an official delegation, and all the way to Paris there were interviews, cheering crowds, and formal ceremonies of honor. King Humbert of Italy bestowed a decoration on Edison and named him a Grand Officer of the Crown of Italy, which, according to one American newspaper, made "Mr. Edison a Count and his wife a Countess." The French President bedecked Edison with the red sash of the French Legion of Honor. At banquets he was hailed as "the man who tamed the lightning" and "the man who organized the echoes." Parisians besieged his Place Vendôme hotel for a glimpse of "the genius of the age."

He toured the Louvre, had lunch at the new Eiffel Tower with Eiffel himself, ate a breakfast of pork and beans with Buffalo Bill Cody, and visited Louis Pasteur in Pasteur's laboratory. The evenings were given over to formal entertainment.

"Dinners, dinners, dinners," Edison said upon his return to the United States. "I looked down from the Eiffel Tower on the biggest dinner I ever saw, given to the mayors of France by the Municipality of Paris—8,900 people dining at one time." Frequently he found himself called upon to make speeches, but he was adept at finding substitutes: the politician Chauncey Depew on one occasion, and Whitelaw Reid, the American Ambassador to France, several times.

The Edison exhibit at the fair was magnificent: a display of telegraphs, phonographs, electric lights, underground conductors, electric motors, and much else. Its central feature was an enormous incandescent lamp, 40 feet high and mounted on a pedestal 20 feet square; on one side it showed the American flag in red, white, and blue lamps, on the other the French flag, while in front was the inscription, "Edison—1889," in glowing bulbs. Atop the pedestal also was a bust of the inventor surrounded by tiny lights. Within the base was a switchboard, where an operator was posted to manipulate the smaller lights and create shifting patterns that enhanced the effect of the single great lamp above.

In front of this display were tables bearing Edison's stock tickers, multiplex telegraphs, vote recorder, electric pen, and dozens of the other early inventions. Elsewhere were the motors and meters. A full miniature Edison electrical distributing system was in place—feeders, mains, junctions, and all. Several dynamos were in operation, running a complete three-wire system. Nearby was a "Phonographic Temple" at which long lines formed each morning when the fair opened, for the phonograph was always the Edison invention of the greatest instant impact.

Shy and close-mouthed under this avalanche of praise and attention, Edison tolerated the crowds, the banquets, the speeches, and the reporters, but was pleased to move on to Berlin for visits with the physicist Hermann von Helmholtz and the electrical inventor Werner von Siemens. Late in September Edison reached London, which he had not seen in nearly seventeen years. He inspected the Edison central station at Holborn Viaduct, whose d.c. power plant had a reach of a mile and a half. But a.c. haunted him even here; Edison was taken to see a huge unfinished a.c. generator that would shortly be sending power at 15,000 volts over long distances into London on another distribution system. "Too ambitious," he said, restating his belief in the safety of his 110-volt system.

On October 6 he was back in New York. Immediately he went to West Orange and entered a darkened room in which his men had installed the first working model of a device Edison had sketched out before his departure. His laboratory assistant, W. K. L. Dickson, switched on a phonograph and began to turn a crank on the new machine. The wavering image of Dickson appeared on a projection screen, raised its hat, smiled, and seemed to say, "Good morning, Mr. Edison, glad to see you back. I hope you are satisfied with the *Kineto-phonograph*." Edison, his long struggle with electricity concluded, was about to give the world the motion picture.

But even as this new project attracted him, unfinished business on the last one presented itself. Edison's patent suits against Consolidated Electric and United States Electric, the holders of the Sawyer-Man and Maxim incandescent patents, were coming finally to new trials. The cases had been working their way through the courts of appeals since 1886.

The adversaries had changed somewhat during the course of the battle. In 1886 Westinghouse had bought control of United States Electric, Edison's main opponent, and soon after he gained an interest in Consolidated Electric as well. Now the suit amounted to a direct legal confrontation between Edison and Westinghouse.

The first suit had been brought by Consolidated Electric Light against an Edison subsidiary, McKeesport Light Company, after an earlier suit by Edison against Consolidated had been thrown out in St. Louis. Consolidated charged that Edison's incandescent lamp was an infringement on the Sawyer-Man patent. Edison, who had seen so much patent litigation that he despaired of all justice, had lost faith in the entire system. He fully expected some kind of chicanery to deprive him now of his essential patent.

On October 4, 1889, Justice Bradley of the United States Circuit Court at Pittsburgh ruled in favor of the Edison lamp over the Sawyer-Man lamp. Admitting that Sawyer and Man had devised an electric lamp that would glow for a few minutes, though it had been without commercial value, he declared:

> They were following a wrong principle, the principle of small resistance in an incandescing conductor, and a strong current of electricity; and . . . the great discovery in the art was that of adopting a high resistance in the conductor with a small illuminating surface and a corresponding diminution in the strength of current. This was accomplished by Edison . . . and was really the grand discovery in the art of electric lighting, without which it could not have come into general use in houses and cities. . . . But for this discovery electric lighting would never have become a fact.

The Sawyer-Man patent was dead, but Hiram Maxim's incandescent lamp, controlled by Westinghouse, was still in use. The United States Electric Lighting Company, Westinghouse's subsidiary, manufactured these lamps for the growing Westinghouse system. The Maxim lamp was also licensed by the other companies that sold incandescent lighting, Brush Electric and Thomson-Houston.

The last two firms had consolidated in that same month of October, 1889. Charles Coffin of Thompson-Houston had found his company on a collision course with Brush that would inevitably lead to another patent fracas. When Brush served notice of an infringement, Coffin simply sent a messenger to

Cleveland, empowered to offer more than three million dollars for a controlling interest in Brush. The offer was accepted, causing no little concern in the offices of Westinghouse Electric and Edison General Electric. By absorbing Brush, Coffin had turned Thomson-Houston into the strongest and soundest electrical company in the country. In terms of sales it now was equal to Edison General Electric and the superior of Westinghouse; in terms of earnings it was unmatched.

Now Westinghouse and Thomson-Houston between them owned virtually all the non-Edison patents in their industry. As the climax of the patent dispute arrived, then, the conflict was a three-sided one, but essentially it amounted to Westinghouse and Thomson-Houston working together to overthrow the Edison patent.

The final suit began on October 15, 1889. After the Bradley decision, it might have seemed that Edison's ultimate triumph was assured, and indeed the legal advisers of Westinghouse and Thomson-Houston were suggesting an out-of-court compromise. But neither Coffin nor Westinghouse was willing to compromise; the struggle had become too intense. Even at the risk of being driven from the electrical field, they had to pursue the litigation to its conclusion.

The opponents were the Edison Electric Light Company (which had recently been merged into Edison General Electric) as complainant, and the United States Electric Lighting Company as defendant. The charge was alleged infringement on Patent Number 223,898, of January 27, 1880, which stated Edison's claims for an electric lamp consisting of a high-resistance carbon filament in a sealed glass container that formed a nearly perfect vacuum. The case had dragged on for more than three years, and its testimony already filled many large volumes when the new round began.

Richard N. Dyer, a well-known patent attorney, headed Edison G.E.'s legal staff. He was assisted by Grosvenor P. Lowrey, the veteran lawyer, and another lawyer named Clarence A. Seward. Chief of counsel for United States Electric was "General" Samuel A. Duncan, aided by Edmund Wetmore.

The defense relied on two main points. First, it insisted that the Edison patent was invalid because its description of the invention was insufficient to enable a person "skilled in the art" to make incandescent lamps by following the directions, a necessary aspect of any valid patent. Second, it claimed that even if lamps could be so made, Edison's work lacked originality, since he had been preceded by Sawyer, Man, Maxim Farmer, and others.

Edison was called to the stand himself. Duncan attempted to destroy his reputation by showing the gaps in the inventor's theoretical knowledge. It was not a pleasant experience for Edison; he could barely hear the questions, found Duncan's slyness infuriating, and greatly longed to be back in West Orange working on his motion pictures. This trial had ceased to seem like his own battle, now that he had sold his companies out to Edison G.E. But he warded off Duncan's charges deftly and emerged from the courtroom unscathed.

To demonstrate that the patent text did contain a complete description of how to make an Edison lamp, Dyer called as a witness John W. Howell, chief electrician of the Edison Lamp Company and a member of the original Menlo Park team. In the presence of officers of the court, Howell kneaded lampblack and coal tar into putty, rolled it out on a plate of ground glass to the hairlike diameter of a bulb filament, cut off short pieces, wound them into spiral form, carbonized them, and sealed them into vacuum bulbs. He made twenty-seven lamps, which when tested burned for six hundred hours. The lamps and Howell's tools were entered as exhibits for the prosecution, and one of the defense's two chief contentions was crushed.

On July 21, 1890, Dyer called to the stand Charles L. Clarke, who had been the acting chief engineer of Edison Illuminating until 1884. Clarke's role was to show that Edison's work was a genuine innovation, not merely a variation on the fundamental work of other inventors.

For nearly three months Clarke testified tirelessly as Dyer, the Edison lawyer, drew from him an extraordinarily detailed account of the incandescent lamp. Then Duncan took over for the defense, cross-examining in the hope of finding some inconsistency, some flaw, some error in Clarke's testimony.

Clarke parried more than six hundred of Duncan's questions in a duel that lasted for weeks. He quoted from dozens of published articles and technical books, repeated earlier testimony without stumbling, and met Duncan's thrusts so unshakably that the skilled attorney was left with no line of attack, and had to withdraw.

The decision, when it came on July 14, 1891, was easy to anticipate. Justice William Wallace of the United States Circuit Court of the Southern District of New York echoed the earlier decision of Justice Bradley in affirming the Edison patent. He said:

> It was a remarkable discovery that an attenuated thread of carbon would possess all the long-sought qualities of a practical burner. . . . The extreme fragility of such a structure was calculated to discourage experimentation with it. . . . The futility of hoping to maintain a burner in vacuo with any permanency had discouraged prior inventors, and Mr. Edison is entitled to the credit of obviating the mechanical difficulties which disheartened them. . . . By doing these things, he made a lamp which was practically operative and successful, the embryo of the best lamps now in use.

But legal harassment had become a way of life for Thomson-Houston and Westinghouse. The Westinghouse lawyers caused the subsidiary, United States Electric, to appeal the decision to the United States Circuit Court of Appeals. Here, at last, the matter came to an end on October 4, 1892, when the higher court upheld the Wallace decision. Edison's use of a narrow filament instead of a thick carbon rod proved to be the pivot on which the case turned; for Edison alone had fashioned the high-resistance, low-current lamp that had been commercially adequate. The higher court held:

> Edison's invention was practically made when he ascertained the theretofore unknown fact that carbon would stand high temperature, even when very attenuated, if operated in a high vacuum, without the phenomenon of disintegration. . . . It was an invention, in the view of the teaching of the art as to the disintegration of carbon under the action of an electric current, to still select that substance as a suitable material from which to construct a burner much more attenuated than had ever been used before. . . . The evidence fails to satisfy us that the prior art furnished any burners less than twice this size. In contradiction to these earlier burners, Edison calls his burner a *filament*.

Victory was complete. Edison G.E. swiftly obtained injunctions prohibiting other companies from manufacturing incandescent lamps without payment of a royalty. But the triumph was a hollow one. It had cost Edison G.E. nearly two million dollars to prosecute the suit. Westinghouse's costs had been almost as great, and the company was all but insolvent. Only Thomson-Houston, which had given moral support to Westinghouse without actually entering the suit, had emerged unharmed. Moreover, the patent itself had only two more years to run. By 1894, every electric company in the land would be free to manufacture Edison lamps without fear of legal penalty. "My electric light inventions," Edison commented bitterly years later, "have brought me no profits, only forty years of litigation."

In the aftermath of the suit, even the victors were left apprehensive. Who knew what fresh courtroom struggles were taking shape already—or who would win them? It might be that the three large companies would destroy themselves in lawsuits as their cutthroat competition continued.

Consolidation seemed the best solution to the problems of the electrical industry. The concept of antitrust legislation was only in its infancy; the customary method of escaping from destructive competition was to form a monopolistic corporation too powerful to suffer from such deplorable manifestations of free enterprise. So it was that between the time of Justice Wallace's decision in 1891 and its affirmation by the higher court fifteen months later, a consolidation was effected.

Henry Villard, who had put many companies together into Edison General Electric in 1889, had even then had a much greater merger in the earliest stages. Villard, reshaping the electrical industry on behalf of his German backers, often cited the cynical axiom of an apocryphal tycoon who declared, "Our business thrives on competition; let us therefore devour some more competitors," and looked about for a likely victim. He selected Westinghouse.

The Westinghouse company, with its Tesla a.c. patents and its spirit of eager experimentation, held important technological advantages, Villard knew. Though no engineer, he was aware that Edison was in the wrong on the subject of direct current, and he wanted to get Edison G.E. somehow into the more adventurous new means of transmission. A merger with Westinghouse was the quickest way. Besides, Westinghouse was still small enough to be absorbed into Edison G.E. without any surrender of control on Villard's part; whereas, if Villard were to try to merge with a big firm like Thomson-Houston, he would be forced to give Charles Coffin a voice in running the combined company.

So during 1888 and 1889, at a time when the public feuding between Edison and Westinghouse was at its most bitter, Villard was secretly talking merger with George Westinghouse.

The negotiations went well, and it seemed that a consolidation would shortly take place. How Villard planned to explain such a development to Edison is unknown, but it would have been difficult.

Then came the first patent victory, in October of 1889. It could be only a matter of time, Villard realized, before the final triumph of the Edison patents was assured. Immediately he changed his tactics and broke off the negotiations with Westinghouse. He turned toward a merger with Thomson-Houston after all.

True, it would mean giving Coffin and his people a large stock interest in Edison G.E. But, fortified with the patent victory, Villard was sure that he could dictate terms to Coffin that would be favorable to the Edison group. After all, Coffin would surely see that Thomson-Houston's own position now was uncertain; Edison G.E., with its stranglehold on the patents, could force its competitors entirely out of business before the patents expired. Villard hoped that Coffin would admit this and accept the merger on his terms. Combined, they could crush Westinghouse and achieve a monopoly.

Edison got wind of Villard's plans and fiercely opposed any such consolidation. He asked Villard,

> Why should we divide? Why hire Thomson-Houston Company to do our business . . .? The more I figure the "benefits" of a coalition the more worried I am that you may be induced to enter into one. . . . The more I figure, the more fatal it seems to me to the Edison G.E., being the dominant electrical company in the country, not only in prestige but in profit. . . . If you make the coalition my usefulness as an inventor is gone. My services wouldn't be worth a penny. I can only invent under powerful incentives. No competition means no invention. It's the same with the men I have around me. It's not money they want but a chance for their ambition to grow.

Nevertheless, the imminent victory of Edison G.E. in the second patent suit gave Villard a strong hand to play. In January, 1891, he tried to make it even stronger by selling $3,000,000 in new Edison G.E. stock to raise additional working capital. Once the company had its patent rights cleared, it would launch into a program of expansion that would terrify the competitors. A month after the sale of this new stock, Villard made his first overtures to Thomson-Houston.

Late in February, 1891, the superintendent of the Thomson-Houston factory at Lynn, Massachusetts received a telephone call from Charles Coffin. "Watch for the arrival at the factory of . . . Mr. Henry Villard, President of the General Electric Company," Coffin said. "Mr. Villard is to be shown through our plant and is to be introduced to Professor Thomson. . . . Please see that his identity does not become generally known."

Villard was taken about the factory quietly, and was pleased with what he saw. The Thomson-Houston executives felt quiet optimism. They wanted the merger as much as Villard did, and they were even willing to accept terms more favorable to Edison G.E. than to their own company. At that moment Coffin privately agreed with Villard that Edison G.E. was in a superior position. The Edison company controlled most of the distribution patents and soon would have undisputed control of the lamp patent. If it wished, it might be able to shatter Thomson-Houston before those patents ran out. On the other hand, Thomson-Houston had valuable transformer patents which could help Edison G.E. overcome the lead of Westinghouse in a.c. technology. The merger seemed logical to both parties.

Spring and summer went by. In July, the Edison lamp patent was affirmed by Justice Wallace. Secret merger conferences took place at the Boston residence of Hamilton M. Twombly, son-in-law of W. H. Vanderbilt. Twombly had been one of the founders of the original Edison Electric Light Company, and now represented the large Vanderbilt family holdings of Edison G.E. stock. Through the hot months of 1891 Twombly conferred with Coffin.

That summer had brought other developments besides the Edison patent victory. The financial world was unsettled by the failure of a large London bank, and credit became tight. There were rumors that Edison G.E., saddled with the great load of debt Insull had contracted for it, was in serious trouble. The rumors were generally exaggerated; Insull, that expert juggler, was managing to meet the company's bills. But the high legal expenses of the patent suits had drained the treasury of Edison G.E. Thomson-Houston, which had not incurred any legal expenses at all, and which through its policy of infringement on doubtful patents had avoided heavy research expenses, suddenly appeared to be far stronger financially than the Edison company that wanted to buy it out.

Villard's position also was being undermined. J. P. Morgan, who was as always a powerful stockholder in the Edison company, feared that the flashy Villard might be riding toward another fall. Morgan was dissatisfied with Villard's performance, and was looking for a way to get rid of him. When Twombly began to negotiate the merger with Coffin, he was supposedly acting on behalf of Villard; actually he was working under instructions from Morgan.

Coffin showed Twombly the Thomson-Houston accounts. Twombly, looking over the ledgers, came to the disturbing conclusion that Thomson-Houston was sounder than Edison G.E. Coffin, by this time, had come to the same conclusion, and turned down the terms that Villard had earlier proposed. "We don't think much of the way the Edison company has been managed," said Coffin.

Twombly returned to 23 Wall Street with this news. Morgan immediately summoned Coffin to New York for a parley. He came in December of 1891, bearing a sheaf of comparative statistics on Thomson-Houston and Edison G.E. This is what Morgan saw:

	Edison General Electric	Thomson-Houston
Capitalization	$15,000,000	$10,400,000
Gross business	10,940,000	10,304,500
Profits	2,098,000	2,700,000
Number of employees	6,000	4,000
Factory space, sq. feet	400,000	340,000
Customers	3–4,000	3–4,000
Central stations	375	870
Isolated installations	2,300	very few
Street railways equipped	180	204
Street railway cars	2,230	2,760

The Edison company had a capitalization half again as great as Thomson-Houston's, yet it was no more profitable than the smaller company, and needed 50 per cent more employees to produce the same volume of sales. Morgan, who had presided over the watering of Edison's G.E.'s stock in 1889, could not have been surprised to find that Thomson-Houston showed a better rate of return on its invested capital. But he was troubled to see that Coffin's company appeared to be more efficient as well.

The banker quickly reversed Villard's intentions. Instead of buying out Thomson-Houston, Morgan told Coffin, Edison G.E. would choose to sell out itself. Together they worked out new terms for the merger under which Coffin's group would have majority control.

The new corporation would be capitalized at $35,000,000. Of this, Thomson-Houston would receive $18,400,000 in new stock, and Edison G.E. only $15,000,000. The official reason for the discrepancy was the existence of $3,500,000 of Edison

G.E.'s floating debt, contracted by Insull, which the new company would have to honor. But actually Morgan's main motive in letting the smaller corporation absorb the larger one was to get rid of Villard. In any event Morgan himself would continue to be the banker for the new company, so his position was unchanged.

Morgan sent for Villard and informed him that his "courteous resignation would be courteously received." Villard, aghast at the terms of the merger which Twombly, Morgan, and Coffin had arranged behind his back, and shaken by his own blunt dismissal, found that he had no weapons at his command. The heavy indebtedness of Edison G.E. could not be denied, and Morgan would use it, if necessary, to crush the company. Villard resigned.

On April 15, 1892, the formalities of the merger were consummated. The new corporation would be called simply the General Electric Company; Edison's name was dropped altogether. Charles Coffin became president of the new G.E. and Eugene Griffin of Thomson-Houston was named vice-president. The only man in the Edison organization who received a high executive post in G.E. was Samuel Insull, who was offered the second vice-presidency at a salary of $36,000.

The board of directors likewise reflected the wholesale sweep. Nine of the eleven places went to the Morgan-Coffin group. Morgan, Griffin, and Coffin all were elected to the board, and Twombly became its chairman. The Edison group was represented on the board only by Edison himself and Frank S. Hastings, one of his newer associates. Most of the Edison executives were dropped from the company.

Insull and Edison were amazed by their abrupt and nearly total ejection. Edison had two sources of bitterness: that his name had been discarded, and that the Edison Lamp Company, which he had hoped might be left out of the consolidation and under his control, was swallowed up in the merger. When news of the loss of the lamp company reached him, it came not from Coffin and Morgan but from a New York newspaper asking for comment. "I had never before seen him change color," said his secretary, A. O. Tate, afterward. "His complexion was naturally pale, but following my announcement it turned white as my collar."

Edison sent for Villard and Insull, and a rancorous scene followed. Edison accused both men of having represented his interests poorly. Villard turned upon Insull sharply and said, "If it had not been for you, Insull, this move would not have been necessary." He meant that Insull's willingness to incur a heavy corporate debt had forced them to accept such unhappy terms.

But recriminations were pointless now. Villard withdrew to other business activities, a wealthier and a wiser man. Insull, who could not bring himself to work under Coffin, took a post as president of the Chicago Edison Company, thereby launching his spectacular and ultimately disastrous career as an entrepreneur of public utilities. And Edison, though deeply wounded, was willing enough to withdraw from the electrical field. He had been on his way out, anyway; he did not mind leaving, but he resented being forcibly discarded.

He had written to Villard in 1890, when the first talk of a merger leaked out, that "it is clear that my usefulness is gone. . . . I would now ask you not to oppose my gradual retirement from the lighting business, which will enable me to enter into fresh and congenial fields of work." And indeed his usefulness was gone. He had lost interest in electricity and had lost touch with recent technical developments. It was better for him and better for the company that he step down and turn toward other research. He had acknowledged that in 1889 by selling out to Edison G.E. and accepting a 10 per cent interest in the company. What happened in 1892 merely completed the process by reducing his stake in electricity to a small investment in General Electric and a meaningless place on the board of directors.

A headline in a New York newspaper summed the outcome up:

MR. EDISON FROZEN OUT

He Was Not Practical Enough

For the Ways of Wall Street

sixteen

The
Aftermath

A **POWERFUL** new company had come into being, one that enjoyed the benefits of Edison's brilliant early work without being held back by Edison's later conservatism. Westinghouse had a fourth of the electrical business; General Electric had all the rest. G.E. combined the Edison company's dominance in incandescent lighting and central station technology with its own strength in arc lighting and a.c. equipment. There would be no more costly patent suits, no more frenzied and destructive competition.

Westinghouse, frozen out as much as Edison himself was, had to fight for existence. Quickly, a non-infringing Westinghouse lamp was devised; it was inferior to the Edison lamp, but it would keep the company alive until the Edison patents ran out two years hence. One of the first tests of the Westinghouse company came in March of 1893, during the struggle for the contract to erect a hydroelectric system at Niagara Falls.

The Niagara Falls project went back to 1890, when a corporation was formed for the purpose of harnessing Niagara's power and transmitting it to the city of Buffalo, twenty miles away. The original scheme had not even involved electricity. It called

261

for erecting waterwheels at Niagara that would generate mechanical energy, which would be transmitted to Buffalo by compressed air, by water under pressure, by some arrangement of wire or rope, or by any other means that would turn engines in the city's factories. Of course, this long-distance transmission of mechanical energy was unsound. But in 1890 it seemed at least as feasible as long-distance transmission of electrical energy.

In 1891, practical long-distance electrical transmission was demonstrated at Frankfurt-am-Main, Germany. Motors were driven and electric lamps were supplied with power generated by a hydroelectric plant one hundred ten miles away. Transmission, naturally, was by high-voltage alternating current. This led to the immediate suggestion that a similar system be installed at Niagara.

Among those consulted was Edison, who was in Europe at the time. "No difficulty transferring unlimited power," he cabled. "Will assist. Sailing today." Edison naturally recommended a d.c. system at Niagara, and withdrew when his idea was rejected. Many other proposals were advanced. By 1892 the contest had come down to a competition between Westinghouse and General Electric for an a.c. system. Westinghouse's ideas were accepted, finally, and after considerable complication the system was put into operation in 1895—the most dramatic demonstration thus far in the United States of the advantages of a.c. transmission over the outmoded Edison-favored d.c.

The Chicago World's Fair in 1893 marked the triumph of electricity. Only a generation had passed since the fair at Philadelphia in 1876 had offered a few tiny, tentative displays of arc lights and dynamos; here, to celebrate the four hundredth anniversary of Columbus' voyage, electricity was king. In the great Electrical Building rose a "majestic luminous column," studded with thousands of Edison incandescent lamps. Edison lights brightened the giant Manufacturers and Liberal Arts Building, the "largest room in the world." Searchlights built by General Electric illuminated the graceful, dancing sprays of the fountains at night. A complete electric elevated railroad, installed by G.E., encircled the exposition grounds. A General Electric dynamo on display was the largest ever built, with a horsepower capacity equal to two hundred fifty of Edison's Long-waisted Mary Anns or thirty of his Jumbos. It produced 1500 kilowatts of direct current; the generator weighed 90 tons, and the flywheel of the engine, 24 feet in diameter, weighed 80 tons.

A motor-driven sidewalk 4300 feet long carried six thousand seated passengers an hour at six miles an hour. It was driven by twenty-four G.E. railway motors of 15 horsepower each. On the artificial lakes and lagoons, fifty G.E. electric gondolas, their power supplied by Brush storage batteries, moved gracefully back and forth.

Westinghouse, too, displayed equipment and lighting systems, and though its displays were not as gaudy as G.E.'s, they won considerable acclaim. And it was to Westinghouse that Insull, now running Chicago Edison and bearing little love for G.E., awarded a large contract for new equipment for his power company.

It was a time of booming growth. One advantage of the consolidation was the elimination of chaotic helter-skelter development in the industry and the substitution of uniform engineering standards. In Philadelphia, for example, more than twenty electric light systems were in operation in the 1890's, variously based on the Brush, Maxim, Edison, Sawyer-Man, and Westinghouse patents. The direct-current companies offered power at 100, 110, 220, and 600 volts. There was also single-phase, two-phase, and three-phase alternating current at frequencies of 40, 60, 66, 125, and 133 cycles. A man moving from one side of the street to another might find that none of his old electrical appliances worked at his new locations. But now, out of this tangle of conflicting equipment, a single pattern was emerging, and the two surviving companies profited greatly as they offered replacements for the obsolete apparatus.

On February 1, 1893, General Electric issued its first annual report:

> The prices at which apparatus and lamps are now furnished by the General Electric Company . . . are, in many instances, lower than those which prevailed prior to the sustaining of the lamp patent, while the quality and efficiency of the apparatus are largely increased. Thus the licensees are enabled to cheapen their production, and their prosperity is greatly enhanced. . . .
>
> On February 1, 1892, the largest power-generator manufactured was of 275 horsepower. Machines of 2000 horsepower are now being manufactured by your company. . . . The largest lighting generators in use on February 1, 1892, were capable of supplying only 2000 incandescent lights each. There are now being constructed generators of the direct-coupled type with a capacity of 12,000 incandescent lights from each engine.

More than two million bulbs were sold in 1892.

A financial panic late in 1893 interrupted this period of growth. Business fell off, and interest rates rose. President Coffin of G.E. found himself with a net indebtedness of $8,734,000. Insull enjoyed a bit of revenge on his tormentors when he forced G.E., strapped for cash, to sell him its giant World's Fair dynamo at a fraction of its cost. But Coffin pulled the company through by liquidating its portfolio of local power utility securities, selling off the stocks and bonds to the stockholders at a third of their estimated value. By the middle of 1894, the panic was over and the company was thriving again. Within four years, it was showing annual sales of $15,000,000, and was able to resume the dividend payments that had been omitted during the period of hard times.

Not only the manufacturers but the power companies themselves were experiencing steady growth. In New York, Edison Illuminating had come through a catastrophe on January 2, 1890, when a short circuit at Pearl Street caused a fire that destroyed most of the station. Only one of Edison's Jumbo dynamos was spared, and, as one Edison man said sadly, "The glory of the old Pearl Street Station, unique in bearing the impress of Mr. Edison's personality, and, as it were, constructed with his own hands, disappeared in the flame and smoke of that Thursday morning." But power service was interrupted only for half a day before neighboring stations took up the load. In 1893 Edison Illuminating added its fifth power plant, at 53rd street, and new ones followed in 1895, 1896, 1898, 1899, and nearly every year for more than a decade thereafter. The first experimental a.c. installation on the Edison system in New York was put into service in 1896, and before long the heresy had firmly established itself. The number of customers passed the ten thousand mark early in 1899; by then, more than five hundred thousand incandescent lamps were on the system. Another innovation in New York was the acquisition of the first steam turbines in 1895, marking the beginning of the end for the old reciprocating engines of the pioneer days. Turbine generators permitted an output of energy that would have been considered fantastic only a few years before.

The story was the same elsewhere. Within his first forty-two months at Chicago Edison, Insull increased the utility's annual power sales from 2.8 million to 13.7 million kilowatt-hours. At the same time, he cut rates steadily, from an original 20 cents per kilowatt-hour to 10 cents in 1897, 5 cents in 1906, 2½ cents in 1909. Between 1890 and 1905, the amount of electric power available in the United States increased hundred-fold.

The arc light vanished although, curiously, its demise came only after a period of late growth. Edison Illuminating began to offer arc light service in 1889 to 110 lamps; it added more each year until a peak of 43,000 was reached in 1908, and then the decline set in, service dropping to 12,800 by 1922 and continuing to drop thereafter. Today the arc light as a means of public illumination is extinct, though it still has industrial uses.

Another casualty of technology was the Edison filament. Squirted cellulose, which had replaced carbonized bamboo, was itself replaced in 1906 by tungsten, now in almost universal use.

Where was Edison during this era of lusty expansion for the electrical industry?

He was busy in other pastures. He was deep in the business of manufacturing phonographs and records, reaping handsome returns—handsome enough to keep him out of bankruptcy in 1899 upon the collapse of a disastrous venture into a project for extracting iron ore from low-yield rocks.

Then came motion pictures. He had toyed with movies as early as 1887; by 1889 he had a device that made the images move. He was unaccountably slow in filing a patent on it, however, and lost millions thereby. In 1893, he wrote of constructing "a little instrument which I call the Kinetoscope, with a nickel and slot attachment. Some 25 have been made, but am very doubtful if there is any commercial feature in it, and fear that they will not even earn their cost."

They earned their cost—a few million times over. As usual, Edison was balked by rival inventors, but did quite well anyway. He left it to others to develop the projector, and had to come to terms with them later on. But the profits were enormous, as they were in the phonograph business until others perfected the disk records that replaced Edison's cylinders.

His bitterness over the end of his career in electricity gradually ebbed. Always an honest man with himself as with others, Edison had come to realize that his day had passed there, that the time of the formally trained engineer had come. He had created a revolution, but he could not direct its later phases, its epoch of theoretical complexity. His rough trial-and-error methods had served their purpose magnificently; now different methods, different men, had to take over. Such researchers as

General Electric's Charles Steinmetz and Irving Langmuir were leading the way to new electrical and electronic miracles that were not merely beyond Edison's scope but beyond his comprehension. One despairing day in 1892, Edison had told an assistant at West Orange to consult a certain mathematician about a technical point. "He knows far more about [electricity] than I do," said Edison. "In fact, I've come to the conclusion that I never did know anything about it." In context, that gloomy outburst was an exaggerated self-dramatization; in a few years it was a more nearly accurate statement of the facts. Edison had ceased to be at home in electrical research.

Early in the new century he noticed that General Electric stock had risen to $330 a share. "If I hadn't sold any of mine what would it be worth today?" he asked a friend. The other man paused to calculate, and replied, "About four and a quarter million dollars." Edison meditated on that for a moment. Then he grinned and said, "Well, it's all gone, but we had a hell of a good time spending it!"

It was not really all gone, however. He entered his seventh decade as a wealthy man, with a crowded lifetime of success behind him, and his fortunes grew to the end of his long life. He became a kind of homespun sage, uttering oracular remarks at West Orange that were applauded throughout the nation for their down-to-earth practicality. Though he had ceased to occupy a place in the vanguard of technical progress, he had become an authentic folk hero.

That status was confirmed in 1904 at the St. Louis Exposition, another of the World's Fairs whose dates form milestones in Edison's career. It was now the twenty-fifth anniversary of the invention of the incandescent light, and Insull's Association of Edison Illuminating Companies gathered an exhibit of "Edisoniana" at the fair. Here, already a quaint relic of a past epoch, was an 1879 dynamo. Here were early lamps and other relics of that pioneering year. And here was Edison himself, white-haired, stocky, vigorous, salty in speech, America's "most useful citizen," hailed by all. He endured another round of banquets and commemorative speeches in this anniversary year, and added more medals to his already large collection.

His connection with the power industry, by then, consisted of no more than the name "Edison" in the names of local utilities throughout the land. Yet from time to time his interest revived. For his friend Henry Ford, Edison tried to design a storage battery that would operate an automobile. Recharging such batteries would have created a large and constantly expanding market for the power companies. In 1905 Edison told the press,

> I believe that the problem of vehicular traffic in cities has at last been solved. The new electric storage cell weighs 40 pounds per horsepower hour. The present lead battery of the same efficiency weighs from 85 to 100 pounds. I believe that the solution of vehicular traffic in cities is to be found in the electric wagon. Leaving off the horse reduces the length of the vehicle one-half. Electric power will double the speed. With the new electric wagon, the vehicular traffic of cities can be increased four times without producing any more congestion than at present. . . . The new storage cell will last from six to eight years. That is proved by actual experiments. I have one cell which has been in constant use for more than five years. The new cell will not cost more than the painting and the tires of the wagon. I do not think the cost of operation will be quite as great as the cost of horses. There again we shall have an advantage.

Edison's announcement was half a century premature. Horses were displaced, but by the gasoline engine, and little came of the plan for an "electric wagon." Only in the 1960's, with air pollution menacing every city, has serious research resumed on a battery that can power an efficient, economical electric car.

In the closing decades of his life Edison came to take on an unreal, larger-than-life appearance. He was used as the central figure of a pulp science-fiction novel, *Edison's Conquest of Mars*, as far back as 1898, and it was this quasi-legendary Edison that the public knew. (In the novel, a popular newspaper serial by Garrett P. Serviss, invading Martians devastate the earth; but Edison invents an "electrical balloon" to take men to Mars, turns out a disintegrator ray and a few other weapons, and leads an interplanetary punitive expedition to the red planet.) So it was that in the First World War Edison was commissioned to conceive super-weapons, and he suggested a series of imaginative military devices that were uniformly pigeonholed by stodgy bureaucrats. Edison no longer was expected to produce real inventions for a real world. He was a figure out of myth, a living science-fiction hero, and it was hard to believe in his actual existence.

It was this same mythological Edison who visited General Electric's plant at Schenectady in 1922 after an absence of twenty-five years. Some eighteen thousand G.E. workers assembled to cheer Edison, and a bronze commemorative plaque was mounted at the door of the laboratory. Steinmetz showed him "lightning bolts," hurling 120,000-volt blasts of energy at a tungsten bar and vaporizing it. "He never mentioned mathematics to me," Edison said, explaining how he got along so well with the hunchbacked genius. Irving Langmuir displayed vacuum tubes for long-distance transmission and a 100,000-candlepower lamp. Edison viewed all these miracles in what must have been a mood of mild awe; yet everything here had its roots in his own achievement.

His last project, inspired by Henry Ford, was the scheme to extract rubber from goldenrod. He began work in 1927, filling his laboratory at West Orange with samples of weeds from every corner of the world, and within a year had made himself master of every relevant fact. It was the search for a filament all over again, half a century later; his methods, his boyish enthusiasm, his energy were all unimpaired at the age of eighty. By 1929 he had produced enough goldenrod rubber to make a single set of tires for his Model A touring car. Then, that summer, he fell ill. He never regained full strength, but he continued his goldenrod research—interrupted only by such ceremonial functions as the one at Dearborn, Michigan, on the fiftieth anniversary of his invention of the incandescent lamp. "We are just beginning," he said. Death interrupted the frail old man's final researches on October 18, 1931. There was some talk of turning off all electric current throughout the country for a minute, in his memory, but the idea had to be abandoned as impractical. So vital was electricity to the nation that the vast electrical system could not be halted, even for a moment.

Vast it was. Out of the dim red glow of the 1879 bulb had come an industry which, at the time of Edison's death, was serving 86,500,000 Americans, 70 per cent of the population. The Pearl Street power station, by 1931, had multiplied to 3873 central plants, furnishing power for 24,701,972 buildings whose occupants were using 19,600,000 electric irons, 17,313,000 radio sets, 7,360,000 clotheswashers, 7,420,000 toasters, 5,750,000 fans, 5,750,000 percolators, 3,220,000 electric heaters, 1,860,000 electric refrigerators, and 880,000 electric ranges. All of that was Edison's doing.

Today even those statistics are cause for smiles, not for wonder. The generating capacity of America's power plants has grown from 34,000,000 kilowatts in 1932 to well over 200,000,000 kilowatts in the 1960's. Over $50,000,000,000 has been staked by investors in the power industry. Millions of refrigerators and air-conditioners and toasters have been connected to the lines since the day of Edison's funeral, as well as appliances scarcely imagined then—color television sets, waste disposal units, blenders, and more. The power industry is the basic industry of America, and its dimensions dwarf anything Edison may have envisioned in 1878 as he began his work. Some 10 per cent of all U.S. investments in new plant and equipment each year go into the electric power industry, and its output, doubling every ten years, has reached the trillion-kilowatt-hour-a-year level.

Perhaps Edison might have visualized such explosive growth

after all, for he was the eternal optimist, and, until his obsession with direct current seized him, he was always looking far ahead. At the end of his life he was, he said, "much interested in atomic energy, but so far as I can see we have not yet reached a point where this exhaustless force can be harnessed and utilized." He foresaw, though, that "there will one day spring from the brain of Science a machine or force so fearful in its potentialities, so absolutely terrifying, that even man, the fighter who will dare torture and death in order to inflict torture and death, will be appalled, and so will abandon war forever." The atomic power plants now so numerous in the electrical industry would have served to show Edison that "this exhaustless force" could indeed be harnessed and utilized, not merely for destruction but to give light to the world.

In one of his most casual, flippant predictions he was wholly correct. Several years after Edison's death, a customer of the New York Edison Company—successor to Edison Illuminating —received a bill for $2.10, covering his electric service for the previous month. He asked to know how much the same amount and degree of light would have cost him in the days of tallow candles. After much research, the company provided the answer: $185.

Tonight, as sundown travels around the world, the lights will begin to glow, from New York to San Francisco, from Honolulu to Tokyo, from Peking to Cairo. They are Mr. Edison's lights that hold back the darkness everywhere on our planet. In the shadow of the Sphinx, along the banks of the Congo, in the towers of Manhattan, by the waters of Babylon, the instant brightness of the incandescent lamp stands at the service of mankind. Only the rich can permit themselves the luxury of candles.

Sources

The primary source for material on the life and work of Thomas Alva Edison is the underground archival vault at the Edison National Historic Site, West Orange, New Jersey. Here Edison's laboratory records are preserved—3,400 notebooks dating from 1870 to 1931, 1,093 United States patents on his inventions, and some 500,000 letters, memoranda, sketches, newspaper articles, and other documents.

Much useful Edison material is contained in the Museum of Science, Fort Myers, Florida, which opened in February of 1966. This museum, located on the grounds of Edison's former winter estate, displays the oldest existing Edison power plant, installed in Sudbury, Pa., in 1883, along with a collection of incandescent lamps, phonographs, stock tickers, telegraphs, and other Edison memorabilia.

The following works were consulted during the preparation of this book:

Bernays, Edward L. *Biography of an Idea.* New York: Simon & Schuster Inc., 1965.

Bowie, Beverley M. "The Past is Present in Greenfield Village." *National Geographic Magazine,* July 1958.

Bright, A. A. *The Electric-Lamp Industry.* New York: The Macmillan Co., 1949.

Casson, Herbert N. *The History of the Telephone.* Chicago: A. C. McClurg & Co., 1910.

Chamberlain, John. *The Enterprising Americans: a Business History of the United States.* New York: Harper & Row Publishers, 1963.

Coleman, Charles M. *P.G. and E. of California: the Centennial Story of Pacific Gas and Electric Company.* New York: McGraw-Hill Book Co., 1952.

Collins, Frederick L. *Consolidated Gas Company of New York.* New York: Privately printed, 1934.

Galbraith, John Kenneth. *The Great Crash, 1929.* Boston: Houghton Mifflin Co., 1955.

Hammond, John Winthrop. *Men and Volts: The Story of General Electric.* Philadelphia: J. B. Lippincott Co., 1941.

Houston, Edwin J. *Electricity One Hundred Years Ago and Today.* New York: W. J. Johnston, 1894.

Jones, Francis Arthur. *Thomas Alva Edison: Sixty Years of an Inventor's Life.* New York: Thomas Y. Crowell Co., 1908.

Josephson, Matthew. *Edison.* New York: McGraw-Hill Book Co., 1959.

Lewis, Floyd A. *The Incandescent Light.* New York: Shorewood Publishers, 1961.

Loth, David. *Swope of G. E.* New York: Simon & Schuster Inc., 1958.

Martin, T. Commerford. *Forty Years of Edison Service, 1882-1922.* New York: New York Edison Company, 1922.

McDonald, Forrest. *Insull.* Chicago: University of Chicago Press, 1962.

Miller, F. Trevelyan. *Thomas A. Edison.* London: Stanley Paul & Co. Ltd., 1932.

Mitchell, Sidney Alexander. *S. Z. Mitchell and the Electrical Industry*. New York: Farrar, Straus & Cudahy Inc., 1960.

Nevins, Allan, with Frank Ernest Hill. *Ford: The Times, the Man, the Company*. New York: Charles Scribner's Sons, 1954.

———. *Ford: Expansion and Challenge, 1915-1933*. New York: Charles Scribner's Sons, 1957.

O'Neill, John J. *Prodigal Genius: the Life of Nikola Tesla*. New York: Ives Washburn, 1944.

Parsons, R. H. *The Early Days of the Power Station Industry*. Cambridge: Cambridge University Press, 1939.

Passer, H. C. *The Electrical Manufacturers, 1875-1900*. Cambridge: Harvard University Press, 1953.

Sharlin, Harold I. *The Making of the Electrical Age*. New York: Abelard-Schumann Ltd., 1963.

Silverberg, Robert. *Men Who Mastered the Atom*. New York: G. P. Putnam's Sons, 1965.

Singer, Charles, and others. *The Late Nineteenth Century*. (*A History of Technology*, Vol. V.) London: Oxford University Press, 1958.

Swan, M. E. and K. R. *Sir Joseph Wilson Swan, F.R.S.* London: Ernest Benn Limited, 1929.

Thirring, Hans. *Energy for Man*. Bloomington, Ind.: Indiana University Press, 1958.

Wainright, Nicholas B. *History of the Philadelphia Electric Company, 1881-1961*. Philadelphia: Privately printed, 1961.

Index

DATE LOANED

SC583—5M